STRIPPED

A Collection Of Anonymous Flash Fiction
Edited and with an Introduction by Nicole Monaghan

PS Books
Philadelphia, Pennsylvania

Stripped © 2011 by Authors

Published by PS Books, a division of Philadelphia Stories, Inc.

First PS Books Edition, 2011

ISBN 13: 978-1-105-11840-1

Cover Image: "Clothesline" by Anne Buckwalter. © 2011 – used with permission. Visit www.annebuckwalter.com

PS Books
93 Old York Road
Ste. 1/#1-753
Jenkintown, PA 19046
www.psbookspublishing.org

STRIPPED

Dedicated to the memory of Dr. Michael Clark,
Department Head of English at
Widener University, Chester, PA.
Beloved teacher, inspiration, and friend.

Contents

Flash Sex: En(Un)Gender Me
(An Introduction to Stripped)

These stories have been stripped. Author identities, and therefore authorial gender, are a mystery. For now. How might this add to the experience of reading with pure literary wonder?

I know what you might be thinking—that authorial gender doesn't matter. It's always the work, the piece, the flash itself. How it can affect you, make you never forget it, even though it took only minutes to experience, how you're sort of regaining your balance afterward, adjusting your clothes. But wouldn't it be a curious and wondrous thing if, for a year, flash writers remained anonymous and readers experienced their work wondering *Is this written by a man or woman*? Would we be able to differentiate one from the other? How often would we be surprised by the author's gender? How much can writers understand about the opposite sex so that we can flesh them out flashy? Perhaps as readers we can be more fully engaged with our characters, our disbelief more truly suspended, when we know nothing of the author.

Collected here are forty-seven short pieces by some of the most established and award-winning flash writers and emerging ones as well. Perhaps when you read them, the authors' true identities will lurk. Perhaps, in creating unforgettable characters that you will care about, the authors have engendered roles of the sex opposite their own so fully that you'll swear that's who *they* are. Or maybe they entirely embraced their true gender roles and sensibilities. We've mixed things up, so predicting would be more fun. Read. Utterly lose yourself for a bit, and mostly, wonder.

One year after the release date of this anthology, all pieces will be matched to authors at www.writenic.wordpress.com.

IT

Boy-Girl

This guy I know has a thing for them: blue jeans and tanks and the people who wear them. People with knuckled spines and gnarled shoulders and chests that run a mad dash like playground slides. Androgyny, he'll say, and feel fancy. A million newsstands crowd along Broadway. Justin Bieber! He'll clutch his heart like he's made the discovery. His lips are bluish, you'd think he sucked nitrous but it's only age, and yet still he manages that smacking sound, as if every rib-shirted-scrawny-limbed thing came battered and spiced in a takeout bucket. Who isn't hungry? Down the street he'll call out, boy-girl, he's indiscriminate, let me fatten you, I mean, really this guy can't be alone for five minutes.

Nothing lasts and now *Oprah*'s ending. I must have been nine, I watched *General Hospital*; usually I watched *Dancing on Air* with neighbors whose perms smelled like egg salad but for some reason that day it was only me kneeing the rug with photographs of sex parts flashing on screen, anatomical flowers and fists, newborn mice tucked into slick ruddy canoes. Yellow pumps twirling, Oprah sat beside an expert who'd written a book, an anthropologist with an extra X chromosome, and before any audience member could whisper freak they whipped through the near infinite permutations.

What big teeth. This guy has a storybook quality. He's days behind a shave, cast in his own shadow, but soon grooming--like most things--will become less dire. Unnecessary. Whisker growth will slow like the rest of him, except in the ears and nose. Stubble will fade into mangy pockets of cheek. Eating will become an effort. Cataracts will cloud his vision, not that he sees great as it is. I could be an adolescent boy or twenty-something girl. He hacks like a dead man no one could save.

In 1985 the talk show was groundbreaking. It hosted a poly-gender parade. Some guests came dolled up in costume; everyone circled the arm of a lover, spouse or family member, except for one who stood alone. A child. The child could have been my age or twice it. There were no distinguishing markers. This child took the last seat on Oprah's panel and refused a blended pronoun, spoke in the blunted voice of robots and the overly medicated: I am a neuter. Later, I would look up the word in the dictionary and find it in reference to cats and dogs. On TV the neuter rejected sex and all of its trappings, offering instead a futuristic fantasy in which some day humans might learn to procreate autogamously, like freshwater snails.

We spend our lives dying but this guy smells like a hospital lounge. Boy-girl, we are vitamins. My shirt came plastic wrapped in a three-pack, which he bought for me. He fingers the worn cotton, inhaling my skin; I pray the sun won't burn. My cousin, Annie, has a daughter who does not feel pain. It's a real medical condition, I'm told. Any minute she could walk into flames.

That day on television the parents sobbed. Oprah sniffed as cameras cut to the front row where they sat working tissues into twists you'd weave through toes. The child sat there, motionless. Lenses zoomed in on brown shoes, loose trousers, eyes without shimmer, flat gray eyes, eyes that gave nothing, eyes that would never wet.

We could be alley cats the way he's poised to feast. It's disgusting. He claws and I curl my back in defense but he knows what's stirring. Beneath the sex, right. Whatever you call it. I'm crying.

Found Objects

He lifted her modest veil and made that eternal but oft-broken promise. Then he bought their first home. When they stood in front of the old Cooper colonial, sagging on its foundation, all she saw was the peeling picket fence she had always wanted and what the house could become; he saw her face shine, and never imagined he'd stand in court in ten years' time before a judge, explaining why the marriage could not be repaired.

A house can be, however, and they threw their young selves into the renovation with savage enthusiasm. Horsehair plaster coated their hair and furniture for years. Pipes and wiring remained exposed, like clogged arteries and enlarged veins needing medical attention.

The house spit up gifts, too, constantly. In the cold, the old bones contracted and cracks appeared out of nowhere, spidering up the drop ceilings in the bedrooms and along the corners where the walls met. In the heat, the frame swelled, the floorboards stopped creaking, and the cabinets and doors closed again.

In between, it gave them hidden objects. An old buffalo nickel rolled from a loose metal baseboard one day, when his wife was vacuuming. Square-head nails seemed to pop up from nowhere. Rusty, with stories and the detritus of others' lives, they emerged in the strangest of places—from under sinks, along wainscoting cracks, and from light fixtures. Marbles seemed to be rolled out to them by ghostly players—clay, cat's eye, clear—and became a hazard for the babies, when they came along.

The house continued to expand and contract, and the objects kept arriving—toy army soldiers, tiny china doll heads, pencils, chalk, shirt buttons, a ticket to a Ferris wheel ride.

They accepted the gifts, and put them into a tall Mason jar, which he kept on his desk. And later, when he was alone, nowhere near that old house of buried treasure, he would pick up the glass jar, looking at all that remained. Shake it, hear its resonance and assurance. Place it back down gently, wondering what, from their own previous life, would be exposed in the coming seasons.

The Bear

She is reaching around him, past the skin and blood and sonorous breathing. She is up on her tip toes, stretching. It's something, this feeling, to finally be seeking escape. Sometimes we want to hurt, and the pain feels a penance we deserve.

She does not look behind her. She already knows what he looks like in bed—a bald, sweaty bear. When she married him he was thin with normal-sized nails and teeth. She did not know he was so clever, that, inside he was made of fur.

She's tried telling herself the fetus is not a child yet. Maybe he will hit me there instead, she'd thought, and he'll be the one to kill it. That's how horrible she'd become, abetting baby murder.

But rage is hereditary. The sins of the fathers are handed down. She'd seen it, knew what it felt like, the sheer, red sound of it.

She knows this is the tipping point, yet the planet's been askew for several years now. Nighttime no longer fades and the days are all black.

On the top closet shelf, inside her Grandmother's hatbox, she finds the knitting needles. They are steel, silver spears. She still has choices: do nothing, take the baby, herself.

But, she thinks, this is not about her. If she were to kill herself, the bear would still need to eat. He would forage, he would destroy other green forests.

Head and heart—he has them, she thinks. Even bears do. She aims there.

Moratorium

No more reading about the moon as shopworn coin. As lamplight, or seashell. As some vague eye in a veil of clouds, watching over the shamelessness of men. Tides, too. No more tides, since they are influenced by the moon. Not one single wavelet sighing as it reflects the shimmering. No faces compared to moons. No moon-lit souls. No moonscaped battlefields or extinguished seas of lost love. No serving platters, tire swings, fruit of magnolias on the air, empty coffee mugs, the grainy dregs of life, etc. No moon splashes. Ditto moonbeams. No dappling rays or sparkles. No jewelry like moons, especially earrings, the tiniest silver arcs. No dangling. I'm sick of dangling. Either give to something fully, or just walk away--Isn't that what you said to me? No blue, black, new, quarter, gibbous, disseminating, dark-side-of, harvest, hunter, or October moons staring blankly like clocks with hands ripped away in a wine-drenched night, the knuckles unhinged, the nails bleeding like these words. No more fucking moons!
Period.
Hey, you want to know what moon I was born under?
Shut up!
Seriously though, what do you think the moon is made of?
Made of? Sand, wet sand like crumbs of brown sugar, Tuesday evenings, the tracks of a good dog we walked along the dunes. The tracks of good talk, easy orbit, of gravitation. Hell, I don't know. I sit here stupid again, my forehead floating off this table. In a Nebraska motel of all places. Feeling about half sorry, in the dark.

Afterglow

Crystal and her moon-faced children live upstairs. I live downstairs, alone. We both waitress at The Outback, and I take business classes at community college. Crystal doesn't see a need for it. I tell Crystal that pretty soon, I'm going to own the damn place while she'll still be washing the bloomin' onion smell out of her hair each night. We'll see, is all she says while she laughs and blows smoke. She tells me she's not holding her breath. We used to fall for the same guys. I'm a lot younger than Crystal but she's better looking.

Crystal, despite her baggage at home, made herself available to every guy who bought her a drink. To each his own. She said she's settling down now, playing for keeps. Her kids, a boy and a girl, scare me. I've never been good around kids. I just don't know what to say to them.

I can smell their cigarette smoke from the back of the house, where they like to torture the large, one-eyed rabbit they named Pistachio. I've told Crystal it is a goddamn shame what they are doing to a living breathing thing. She always says, "Wait until you have your own, then we'll see." But she never sees things the way they really are.

It's hot out and I am feeling the cumulative effect of so many things. I take three aspirins with a glass of cold beer. I feel sick from the sounds of the rabbit squeals. Crystal and her boyfriend, a man my mother would have called "rogue," are thumping around in the bed, calling God down from his heaven.

Her son throws rocks at the bedroom window that faces out into the back yard. I open my window. I yell "*Stop!*" They laugh hysterically. The rabbit is motionless, his only eye, blood red, frozen in fear, I think of calling the police. I turn on the big fan in the house to block out the noise, and though my skin is moist, though I am shaking with cold.

The rhythmic thumping has stopped. I hear the murmur of their voices in the sweet afterglow before reality sets in. I want to go and rescue that rabbit, but fear grabs me by the throat. I tell myself I don't know what to expect. But my heart knows. I stand at the door. I wrap my arms around my waist. Squeeze myself hard and think it might not be a bad thing to have a man of my own.

Marooned In A Borrowed Mansion

Some of the locals said the house was haunted. Perfect, I thought, we'd be a good match. It sat on a hilltop like a giant ship run aground. The original possessor had a penchant for all things maritime, which seemed odd given the landlocked alpine location.

The truth took months to realize. The beautiful trout pond, and what it reflected, would come to haunt me, adding to the list of shriveled, dormant things moldering behind my gaze.

I called it the boathouse, yet it was mercifully safe from kitschy adornments like portals and ship's wheels. It's beauty lie in gleaming tropical wood floors and cabinetry. The house circled around itself, every room an island.

Curious new friends who came, only came once. Their goodbyes seemed like omens, like farewells; remarking on the smell of pipe smoke in some rooms, a barrier of cold air where no drafts should be.

In town I could be a different person, laughing off the old stories of ectoplasmic sea captains. But in the boat house, even with guests, I startled at hello, let the kettle scream too long, flinched at a kind hand on my shoulder. There is one apparition I fear the most, one no one here knows.

I assumed the caretaker position that autumn to save money I had said; worry less about my own life and restore my sobriety. I knew, though, I was punishing myself in some elaborate and decadent way. I was fully aware of the siren-like effect of trout in the pond, the golden coined aspen whispering in the wind. I spent many days exhuming the game trails and streams on the property, tuning out the news and the radio, becoming more and more obsessed with the serenity and the calm, lulled by the bounty of a stocked freezer and warmth in almost every room.

Slowly, I began to see the pond as a reflection of all the things I couldn't face. The mirrored surface reflecting the house in still time, but when wind troubled the water, a blurred image of her surfaced.

The spooky hollowness began to make sense as I mended, insulated, cleaned and repaired. The groans and lurches of the house were only icemakers and damp wood drying in the thin air, boilers heaving and sighing with every task. It was just wildlife blooming in the attic, drafts dooming the doorways, old hunting clothes permeating the closet. The house was the house. I was merely an interloper, privy to its secrets.

When storms hit I saw myself there, mid-deck, looking down at the mirrored pond. Below, only concentric circles of rising fish disturbed the image of me, the stowaway in the window. Indifferent and plodding, I had been immune to the imagined ghosts while drowning the real ones, over and over again.

I stayed two winter seasons. When the pond froze I could sometimes forget, but with that last spring came too many visions of the home I had left. I saw clearly the child I had abandoned, her grey eyes meeting a dark stranger's, a stand-in for me I supposed. Another day in this house, another dollar in the bank account won't stop her searching for me in every man's eye. Echoes of an abandoned life rang in my ear louder than any forgotten alarm in that house. If I hadn't known it all along, I surely knew it now.

Cisco

I didn't know he'd followed me until I saw the fat balding bus driver kicking my dog like he was something diseased and evil. In the classroom, I kept imagining the sparkle of his tags and how he yelped and cowered away, how no one had ever hurt him before, how he didn't know what he'd done wrong. I kept wishing I'd had a leash even though wishing was useless. The desert rolled by so long and school was a place you had to go, had to leave home for. Cisco waited miles away. The leash would have done no good. I couldn't have walked him home. I kept imagining writing a letter to someone to let them know about the cruelty I'd seen and I didn't remember ever seeing it before. I felt like a coward, crying and not going after Cisco. There were blankets at the foot of the bed where he'd sleep at night when I got home. After he brought our pajamas to us from where mama laid them out in the little hallway room in the trailer. After we dressed, he'd bite hold of the hem of our shirts and tug us toward bed to make us laugh and mind, "Bed Time!" That word turning to joy and fun. I'd mind him. I'd smooth out the blankets and feel the warmth of his body against my feet.

Sculpted

I think of you that way sometimes. A work of art. A moment in low-lighted recess when children and patrons have faded and you've stepped down from your pedestal base, formed yourself alabaster.

Stoned sex poured fluid.

I did not mean to leave you here. Did not mean to chase you through halls and fall into landscapes, slide into abstractions. They surprise me, the abstractions.

Do you believe me?

I dream you surrealist.

Flesh-painted on stiffened gauze, three dimensions of disappearance, thirty-six hours into yesterday when you lay spread and real on a soft, white, cotton sheet.

And as the patrons watch you move through rooms and vestibules—muscle to tendon to joint, motions beneath skin—they study the shapes of you. You sit, Rodin-like, for them. You play with food you will not eat but push to your lips full, un-parted.

Yes, I say, yes.

I dream your mouth too. It is not so surreal as I would not want it to be because I lie to myself, sometimes, in double negatives. I do not tell myself what I do not want to hear. It is a saving distraction.

Do you know? My fingertips find you in low-lightings? Soft, moist corners where your fingers have not been? I tell you this because you must know. You must know of these last places. They are all I have left to offer.

A Conservator In The National Museum Of American History Rigged Into A Suspended Harness Floats Inches Above The Star-Spangled Banner

A star is missing. Someone's souvenir, lost long ago. I am time's shrapnel, saving spaces left out, restoring the nothing to the nothing left over.

HER

Momma

I read baby magazines under the bed while you're at work shaving the tops off mountains. My teeth are loose. I'm old enough to remember switchboards and the intercourse of plugging and unplugging jacks. You're younger. You're stronger. You say, "Old women are so hot," and you only say that because I make you biscuits like your momma's. Your momma went young. I sometimes wonder if all this is just a part of that.

I stack pictures of pregnant young women in a shoebox. I hide a knife in the shoebox too. It's not for you. I turn it on myself, one stab a day in places I can cover with my own folding skin. I realized I was old when I started feeling my flesh weigh on me like a jacket. I've tried not to turn sour, but my body makes it hard. When you grow old you become a god or an insect. I became a cicada. I make so much noise, but when you step on me, all I do is crunch.

I collect antique baby bottles. Today, I cut my tongue and stuck it in one of the bottles to drip. I'm losing all this blood. They say your body makes more. Maybe my body will replace the old blood with young blood. I'll use the old blood to write a letter to the Devil, because God's not listening.

I hear you coming. I put the bottle of tongue blood in the shoebox with everything else. I fold my arms across my chest like Dracula's daughter. I don't move. You pull me out from under the bed by my ankles. You say I'm sticky, like my sweat is glue. You lift me up so that my hair becomes my feet. You shake me, but nothing falls out. I'm already empty of your child.

You lay me out on the bed like a fish, tip to tail. All the fish around here taste like batteries because of the mountain skimming. It's no wonder my womb is a dried arrangement.

You say, "We're too old for a kid anyway," and I say nothing because my tongue is still bleeding. You open my mouth with your thumbs. You see the blood I'm trying to swallow. You kiss me and take the blood as your own. It's not much blood.

You ask if I bit my tongue, so I show you the knife and the scars and the bottles. I show you how not all plans die in the delivery but sometime long before.

Behind The Eight Ball

I was a small mistake. My dad had his tubes tied, or his hole removed or whatever it is that people do. I came way after the fact, behind the radar, my siblings grown and moved into their own drug circles, and halfway houses. Barflys. Losers.

And there I was…stuck. Two gray haired hippies, traveling around the country looking for patches of peace that no longer exist. Every time we'd stop for more than a day, I'd think of ditching that Winnebago, forging out on my own: Fargo, Sacramento, Fairbanks. Anyplace seemed far better than a 10 by 14 foot trailer on wheels. But I barely had a pot to piss in.

My dad, Dusty, said, "You don't need school! Look at that river, the way that hawk soars on the air currents, eyeballing salmon. School? Just makes you jaded."

Mom smoked cigarettes laced with pot, crooning Joni Mitchell songs on her homemade dulcimer: *I am on a lonely road, and I am traveling, traveling, traveling.* Tell me about it. Crafted macramé projects trailing rainbow colored yarn all over the floor. Sometimes I wondered what kind of creepy crawly creatures made their nests with it. I'd draw pictures on the windows of bugs, anthrax, pollywogs. On rainy days, we'd consult her 8-ball, take turns asking random questions. She named it Misty, called it her oracle.

She'd hover over it, rubbing, whispering. "Tell us, Misty, do you think that Debbie will get married before she turns 20?"

We'd flip it over, and in that purplish, bubble-filled circle the answer would pop into view: *Don't Count on It.* That made me happy. I never wanted to marry. The entire idea just creeped me out. Who could stand someone for that amount of time? Who could live with themselves, ignoring these unanswerable questions that churned inside me? No. Not me.

Certain nights after I'd hear Dusty's snore, I'd consult the 8-ball on my own. Nights when I couldn't sleep, the moon slanting onto my sleeping bag. "Is there more than this?" I'd squint my eyes to read it:

21

My Sources Say No.

What the fuck kind of sources are you? I'd shake it again, and look for the real answer. Misty probably fell asleep:

You May Rely on It.

Then I could drift off. Sometimes before I slept I'd rub myself just a little down there. It made me feel... more alive? A little less like I wasn't meant to be here. Like I'm not some afterthought.

The Distance Between The Bridge And The River

The river is not safe for swimming, so the city built a bridge to span it. To get to work, Amanda walks across the bridge. She crosses at 8:22 a.m. and at 5:07 p.m. She walks on the right side of the bridge in the morning and on the left side of the bridge in the evening. She never lingers. She cannot see where the river begins and ends. She thinks the distance between the bridge and the river is not far. Maybe three or four seconds, if that.

If that.

She knows that the distance between the bridge and the river will end with a landing.

On that bridge, love has bloomed and faded; girls in tight bright dresses have smiled next to boys being men in tuxedos; visitors have posed for pictures, the city's sprawl far in the background; and photographers have found meaning in moments. Still, the river is constant; its always-changing nature never changes. Today's river will not be tomorrow's river. Where she'd land today is not where she'd land tomorrow. The city built the bridge so that girls like Amanda could get from one side of the river to the other.

Mornings Amanda carries her lunch in a black sack and a newspaper under her arm. She dresses for her job. Evening Amanda carries back an empty sack. She knows how many steps will take her from one side of the river to the other. She likes the sound her steps make on the bridge. Step. Her right foot. Step. Her left. Step. Step. An echo that she was there.

There.

There.

She doesn't think about how jumping will feel as she crosses the river; she thinks, instead, about what the bridge will look like from below. Odd the things we think about when we decide to say goodbye; what we say when we say goodbye. That there are goodbyes.

Odd knowing that there is no one to whom we need to say goodbye.

One evening, Amanda stops halfway across the bridge. She knew that morning how her evening would end. She chose her white dress because in it she feels light, like she maybe could fly. In the white dress, she is happy. She leaves her black sack on the bridge. She takes off her shoes and leaves them, too. The bridge is warm under her feet. So is the railing.

She does not think about what will come after or next or if landing is the end. Even in the dress, she knows she won't fly.

Still, the landing is nothing without the fall. The fall is nothing without Amanda. Amanda is nothing without the people who will find her. The people who will find her, who will ask why, are nothing without the bridge. The bridge is nothing without the river in which no one should swim.

The distance between the bridge and the water is not far. Maybe three or four seconds, if that.

If that.

Santa Caterina

The woman—a middle-aged American tourist—takes another cigarette from the pack. She doesn't recognize any of the men wandering the Campo, never really expected to. But she's here. To relive a dream. What do they call it? A last hoorah?

The most beautiful moment of her life sneaked up on her decades ago. A pretty twenty-year-old, she followed a parade of young men in tights beating drums and waving flags. It was Siena, the feast of Santa Caterina, but she didn't know that. She was just giggling at cute butts with her girlfriends.

The young men filed into a church, stopped beating their drums in front of a portrait of the saint and began to sing—loud and clumsy; and the woman—still a virgin then—stopped breathing, stunned by the big dumb beauty of men roaring at a saint.

"Scusi," a man—a middle-aged Italian—brushes by her table, upsetting the flower.

"Null problema," she says—the extent of her Italian.

The man sits at the table next to hers, smiles. He's the right type, she thinks. The kind who'd have looked good in tights twenty-five years ago. His lips look like they know how to sing to a saint.

"Are you from here?" She's bold.

He looks up from his cell phone. "Si si, Siena," he says. It sounds like advertising for the city. "Can I help you?"

She smiles, takes a long drag off her cigarette. She's never been this forward.

"Yes, actually. You can."

On the plane to Florence, she worked out her strategy. She'd come clean with the men right from the start. The mastectomy was in three weeks, two days after the feast of Santa Caterina. She had to fit her dream through such a tiny window. Afterward—when her breasts were gone—the memory of feeling like a woman would have to be enough.

She explains her situation quickly and loudly enough for anyone to hear. When she's done she stares into the stunned man's face.

"Dio!" He laughs. "I expect directions to the Cathedral. Or a nice ristorante."

"It's OK." She takes out another cigarette. "Really." She knew it wouldn't be easy.

"No, no." He moves to her table and lowers his voice. "Of course I'll do it." When he smiles, she notices his teeth are not exactly straight and his nose hair is distracting—but he's kind. His food comes. "Are you eating?" he asks.

"I'm not hungry." She hasn't eaten in weeks, but she doesn't tell him this. She doesn't want to feed the cancer. "I'm a little like Santa Caterina, that way." She laughs as he scarfs his bruschetta. He's perfect. His mouth will taste like basil.

He takes her to his apartment. The tights are in a wardrobe. "They're a bit tight," he says and laughs, but he puts them on and parades for her. He pretends to beat a drum and wave a flag. "You have luck with me," he says. "I'm a silly bird." He undresses her, touches her breasts with a tender hand because he knows the pain. His first wife went the same way, but he doesn't tell her this. His kisses are soft and warm.

"The song. Do you still know it?" she asks.

"Si si," he says. "I'm not the best."

"That's good. I don't need the best. I just need—"

He begins to sing in a low baritone, his voice trembling, searching for the melody as he presses against the woman's body. Plodding. Manly. Beautiful.

Jericho Beach

They get lost on the way to the museum because Jeff doesn't trust Marissa's navigation skills. She sits in the passenger seat folding and unfolding the Vancouver map, incisors gnawing the inside of her mouth, the tip of her tongue searching for blood.

"Hey!" says Jeff and she looks up fast because there's a laugh in his voice as he pulls over. His hands loosen on the steering wheel. He's grinning, staring out the window behind her.

She turns and sees what he sees, light glinting off the deep water of the inlet, sun-burnished cargo ships, a beach dotted with thick logs, lounging sunbathers. And beyond all this, snow-crusted mountains, so close they take her breath away.

Jeff points to the highest peak. "That must be Whistler."

She has the map; she could check, *wants* to check, thinks about it, but lets it go.

He drives the car into the parking lot at the end of the road. Through the windshield, she sees teenagers tossing Frisbees on a white flowered field. Something uncoils inside her. Her shoulders relax.

He takes her hand as they stroll toward the beach. They're new to each other, that early time when the softest glance of fingers wobbles her knees, molecules crossing between them with coded messages of desire.

They go on this way, teetering a little, until Jeff angles toward the park, his arm wrapped around her shoulder. She slides her hand under his shirt, between his jeans and skin. A fizz pulses from between her legs, and she buries her face in his sleeve, draws in his dark scent. They cross a bridge, and on the other side, where a copse of trees shades the stream, they stumble down into the tall soft grasses.

The wind has the feel of snow, the sky is dimmed to steel. She pulls her woolen scarf over her mouth and looks across Jericho Beach to the mountains, knowing now, years later, that Whistler is not among the peaks.

She remembers the day they'd gotten lost. She'd say, "Turn right at the next corner," and he'd speed up instead of slowing down. She'd say, "Go back. Go back." but he'd keep going. He'd wound her up as tight as he could like a mechanical toy, the kind with a key and a ribbon spring.

Her chest tightens, as it did then, when she squinted at the map, and saw that yes, yes she was right and said, "*That* was the street," but instead of making a u-turn, he'd gone the opposite way. It was in that moment she'd realized this thing with this man wouldn't work, couldn't work.

She turns now toward the field, a gust of wind stinging her eyes, blurring both the bridge and the naked trees beyond. He'd teased her about how easily her walls had tumbled down on Jericho Beach. Then she'd told him it was over.

The map is her metaphor. The way she held it in her hands, folding and unfolding it in her lap like the middle school game. An origami crystal ball that could be opened and shut as many times as she had to, to come up with the perfect combination of what she wanted and what she didn't.

A shout wheels her around and she smiles. Here he comes, holding paper cups of coffee, striding across the sand toward her, their daughter tagging along with doughnuts.

She waves, her fingers folding and unfolding. As if she could choose.

Chips From The Broken Sky

With her finger, she traced *America* on the back of her other hand, a habit she had always had, even before she immigrated to Paris. He noticed and she stopped, her finger protesting the interruption. He smiled, but she knew he wouldn't ask her out again. She would have said no anyway. He had a mole over his right eye, smaller than the smallest of hers, like a tiny button.

From the beginning, her grandmother had convinced her the wrong touch to a mole and a child could bleed to death. The fear had followed her into adulthood and she never touched her moles, not ever. Nights, she sometimes pressed and counted her bones. Her grandmother also claimed there was a great storm on the day she was born and her moles were chips from the broken sky burned brown by lightning. She told all this to the white-painted brick wall opposite her bed and then counted her inhales until she fell someplace close to sleep.

Mornings, the birds beyond her window woke her with their insistent noise, like the squeak of shoes on dull linoleum.

"You're just homesick," Liz said from Denver. "It'll get better."

"I can taste people's fear here," she told Liz, "Afraid Americans will swallow up France."

"You got away," Liz said, sounding nothing like a best friend.

The air in the apartment changed, colder, heavier, and the white-painted walls seemed less shiny.

After more phone calls home, she drank too much coffee and considered calling in sick to the office. She pushed herself out of her apartment and into filthy Paris, mentally listing all the diseases she felt grateful she didn't have.

On her lunch break, she stole a banana from the open-air market. At least the sun-colored fruit seemed fitting of the 'City of Lights' she'd come all this way to find. She sat on a bench in the park with the banana on her lap and the sun's heat on her head. That morning's coffee gurgled in her stomach. She imagined herself in bed

29

spooning with the banana, its smell getting into her pores, hair, and moles. A man ran across the grass, a dragon kite raised high above his head, a boy toddling behind, laughing. She wondered why kites so captured people's hearts and imaginations. Maybe she needed to fly one to know. She traced 'America' on the back of her hand with the banana's nib. The fruit softened in her palm. When it came time to leave, she tossed the bruised banana into the garbage.

Summer turned into fall and she needed warmer clothes. In the dressing room mirror, she studied herself in the black turtleneck and black wool pants, every mole hidden.

In the corridor, a mother told her daughter it was hard to know what the clothes looked like on "with that hair."

The daughter closed her dressing room door. "You always do this."

"Good times," the mother said.

It seemed sarcasm sounded the same the world over.

They passed her dressing room, the mom saying, "I prefer you natural, that's all."

The sales assistant knocked on her door, was there anything she needed?

She missed fighting with her mother.

The sales assistant knocked on the door again. "*Allô?*"

She heard *hollow*.

Their last fight, on the day before she left, her mother said, "Your problem is you always want more."

She removed the store clothes, and her hand hovered the right side of her stomach and her largest mole. Her fingers hummed and heart felt like a mountain she was about to step off.

Rosalia

People pay to see the little dead girl, good people. Fathers, mothers, children too, some Sicilian, some not. This child, the dead one, keeps her golden curls bright beneath the streets. The perfect daughter, lying there with eyes long closed, sheet tucked tight under her chin. She smells of the tea my granny makes; brown oily fluid that makes me think of bad gravy and overdone beef. But with added dust.

I scuffed my shoes, the pretty ones my mother nagged me to wear, on the stone beside the coffin. Moving the death dust sprinkled there, grey and gritty, some from tourists, some from the mummies trapped below ground. Never to rot, only to perish. I envied them.

She tutted, but I carried on scuffing and scraping, hoping to remove a little more pink, a little more glitter, before she noticed. Fake nails flicked my ear so hard I cried out, and wondered how she could ping me so hard without them flying off. I'd seen false nails lying sometimes on the pavements outside clubs and bars, sometimes pink but often red. Beetle cases, without the legs, but somehow more icky.

I stopped scuffing.

This little girl, Rosalia, had a floppy silk bow in her hair, the colour of caramel ice cream melting in the heat above. It was cooler down here, and dry, and I could feel a tickle building in my throat. My mother fussed with my hair, wiggling the hairband that felt as if it wanted to bisect my scalp, it was so tight. And pink, the pink of sticking plasters and other hated things.

I coughed a little, straightened my skirt, wishing I could rip it off, wondering what Rosalia had on below her dingy blanket. What did two year olds wear in the twenties? My mother was fond of telling me how the sexes dressed alike back then, in "simpler times." Simpler people, more likely.

The guide was explaining in a semi-musical drone that reminded me of the unthinking prayers and retorts my mother offered at church every Sunday that Rosalia was believed to be a doll until recently. Some kind of sick, waxy doll. Then folk at a nearby museum proved she was real. Really dead, really there, really worth the price of a ticket to the gawpers, sickos, and tourists desperate to get out of the heat.

Like my mother.

I squeezed a finger between my neck and the itchy lace collar she'd chosen for me to parade in today. A dirty brown blanket would have suited me fine. It had to be more comfortable than the pink and white confection she was deluding herself with today, and I certainly preferred the colours. Earthy, honest colours, like Rosalia's skin, or my granny's garden.

I coughed again, and realized I needed to go. Badly. My mother was still listening to the guide; his breath belching garlic and herbs over the beef jerky smell of the crowded crypt. Doors to the side held signs of skirts and trousers, flicking a glance at my mother's I sneaked in. Locking the cubicle, I stared at the cistern. Bleach won out over beef, stinking of cleanliness despite the location. I lifted my skirt, and smiled.

Pink shoes slightly apart, I dipped into my panties, and peed.

I wished I could swap with Rosalia, just for a day. Eyes closed, absent. My mother would be happier with a real girl, even a dead one, of that I was sure.

Shaking off the drips, I tucked myself in. Happy to do it the bad way.

Standing.

Seven Happy Endings
For R.S.

One.

I am in a tanning bed, fingering myself, thinking about her. Everything is bright light and beautiful feelings. I don't do drugs, but she does. We are at Bonnaroo, in my thoughts. She's sitting beside me in our tent, talking about the history of Ebonics and her Golden Retriever, who is in training.

"He graduates soon," she says.

"I want to fuck you," I say.

"Let's eat grilled cheeses first," she says.

"Okay," I say.

I think about the sharp way she says "grilled cheeses" as I lie naked in the tanning bed, fingering myself. I listen to synthy music and when I come the beat pounds my chest. I feel new, even though I am not. I am here only because, two days ago, some salesperson sees me sitting outside of Starbucks, feeling depressed after a therapy appointment, smoking a cigarette. This salesperson walks up to me and offers three tanning sessions and four hours of personal training for $30. I think of her, how hurt I feel. I say yes. *Yes!* My heart sings yes as I come, alone, in this chamber of light.

Two.

"No one can ever replace you," she says. She is eating Nerds and sitting on my kitchen floor. "Sit with me," she says, and I do.

"It's hot in here," she says.

I say, to her, "Do you need water?"

"No," she says. "You look beautiful with a tan," she says, and rests her head in my lap.

"I'm Italian," I say. "I'm always tan."

"Everyone can use a tan," she says.

Three.
After she realizes her life is missing many things, I understand the same thing about my own life. She won't call me back or return my texts so I decide to treat myself to some frozen yogurt at Pinkberry. While I'm walking into Pinkberry thinking *chocolate or coconut or both*, I see her in the parking lot. She's wearing a red t-shirt that says, "Trust me, I'm a doctor" I wonder if she is high. I want her to come all over my hair. You know, you can be in a long-term relationship or you can just fuck your friends. I don't want either.

Four.
I see her from time to time, grabbing coffee at Starbucks, going grocery shopping at Trader Joe's, reading at Barnes and Noble. Once I saw her at the farmer's market buying a block of cheese and she gave a small piece to her Golden Retriever and I felt like dying.

Five.
At the personal training sessions I get endorphin-happy, and then I go tanning and finger myself until my sessions run out. Then I go back to therapy. I've been cooking elaborate dinners for myself every night and sometimes I'll even pour myself a glass of red wine. When I go to bed, I think of a stranger's touch.

Six.
"Dissecting an unhappy childhood is an art," she says, finally.
  She cries and I scramble eggs for both of us. She stops crying once the eggs are done. She kicks my shins as we eat.

Seven.

I don't see her anymore. She probably took so many drugs she floated away. Soon I'll adopt my own dog, a Beagle, tell everyone he is graduating from training, have a party for him. His graduation cake can be made of cheese. I can buy a house just for us and we can decorate it with other people's junk. But these plans, they're not my life, yet. I'm enjoying this in-between state. Now it's just me and I am going to do big things with my time.

Gorgo, Queen of Sparta

By her ninth birthday, Gorgo already feels like she's running Sparta. She tells her father, King Cleomenes, not to trust Aristagoros, a visitor from a neighboring land. When she tugs on his robe, Cleomenes bends to hear her, nods solemnly, and sends the Ionian away. It's her first taste of power and it tastes like honey and fresh milk.

When she's thirteen, Gorgo marries her half-uncle Leonidas. Fresh out of school for Spartan youth, she is able to fight him off three nights in a row. On the fourth night, he overpowers her with undiluted wine, fills her with his seed. It is the seed of a Spartan king. She takes it in and allows it to make her stronger.

She's fourteen when she first swells with child. And fourteen still when it goes away. She checks the blood for a baby, but finds nothing. Leonidas rides her forcefully as soon as the bleeding stops. He grunts as he comes, *I will make this one stick.*

It does stick. She gives birth to a son who cries all the time. He spits and wails and changes from pink to purple. Gorgo carries him constantly, lets him fall asleep at her breast. At times, she fears she'll go mad from the sounds of screaming. When Leonidas visits, he tastes her breast milk, asks her to recite everything she's eaten. He brings her poke root and tea with dandelion and blessed thistle. It tastes bitter, but she drinks it.

Her blood comes as reliably as the full moon for four years. Then, when she is nineteen, it stops. Leonidas brings her Yarrow and Chaste Tree berry and Peony root, but it doesn't do any good. *I thought you would bear me more sons*, he says. She replies, *One is all you need.*

While she raises the child, Gorgo's father cuts himself into strips. The wounds run around his body like filigree on a clay plot. Some are old and scabbed over. Some are fresh and red and raw. Gorgo wants to touch them, but she's afraid. What is he trying to let out through all those holes? If his blood is already in her veins, is it also in the veins of her son?

When she gets tired of seeing his scabs, she smuggles a knife past his guards and leaves it, with a kiss, in his palm. What he goes digging for inside his stomach, she'll never know. Perhaps he is looking for another heir, one that will watch his skin unravel like cotton thread until it's long enough to reach across the sea.

Her husband is next. He catches an arrow with his heart in a battle against a million men. He takes arrows to his belly, his legs, his strong shoulders, and his eyes. Her son, Pleistarchus, is named the new king. His cousins steward for him until he is old enough to rule. Gorgo thinks she would make a good king. After all, she is the daughter of a Spartan king, the wife of another, and the mother of a third. She thinks of the people she has loved and lost—Spartan kings, all.

Gorgo sits quietly in the city square. She fetches water for her son and feeds him slivers of bread. She knows her only true purpose is to take care of Spartan kings, to give birth to Spartan kings, and to kiss Spartan kings good-bye when it's time for them to destroy themselves. She has done this twice already. When the time comes for Pleistarchus, she will be ready to do it again.

Eruptions

Avril and Jim Hunt lived in a cottage on the Kenai Peninsula, west of Mount Redoubt. It was April, 1990. Avril had bought their eruption masks, as well as pantyhose for the air filters, after she had laid out long-sleeved clothes and jeans for protection.

The volcano, blow ready, would create an artificial dark soon, a warm sky blurred by pollutant particles, ash drifting down like dirty snow for weeks—which had made this morning's pre-blow sunrise all the more colorful. A bright thing before a pending gray.

"You have what we need?" Jim asked.

"Yes," she said. "Water, food, radios, flashlights, batteries, cash—accounted for." Maybe in Anchorage, she thought, there'd be only a few days of dusty wind, but here, the harsh resultant debris, for a short while, would turn day into night. She knew it wasn't the best time to bring this up, but told Jim, "I am thinking I want an abortion."

Jim stood in the hall, one arm in his flannel jacket, the rest of the garment dangling.

"It's just not working," she announced in a rush of breath. "Can't you see?"

On the news was moment to moment volcano coverage. "Any minute now, watch for it," intoned the broadcaster. "Hey if you aren't ready to evacuate, you better get ready."

"Honey, the other girl meant nothing," Jim said. "A one time, bar girl. I told you that."

"I heard you already."

"So why don't you forgive me?" he asked.

"I did." She dampened several towels for use in the doorjambs. "A long time ago. It's about something else."

"What?"

He waited, but "Can't say," she replied, recalling something else, months earlier, when she had watched that distant mountain through their bedroom window and waited for an unanticipated burst of steam or sign that she and the landscape were connected—when it was cold and without need for evacuation. It was on a morning much like this, not bitterly frosty, when Jim had been gone hours already at the station—as she and Tucker had lain together in her bed and she'd smiled, accepting his differences with a calm sort of take, enjoying the heft of his body upon hers, the sensation of his back hair springing softly against the pressure of her fingers, the feel of his five o'clock shadow rasping her thighs as his head labored below, then noting how his mouth seemed so enormous between her legs, so wet and searching, like her orgasms were explosions themselves, rocketing, near painful.

There'd been no condom. How could one be waited for, she ventured later, when the vibrations of such acts had decreased her tension to threshold, spreading her thighs so wide it seemed that naturally something must come between them? She did not think of Jim in that moment. She thought of herself, erupting. Hot, reactive steam. Jim left her cold.

But she returned to Jim, in the now, when the mountain beside them might really blow, would blow. "I do want the abortion," she said. "Yes. But we can stay together—if you want…"

Jim did not reply until she went to grab her things so they could go. "Is it mine?" he asked.

She said nothing. Both answers meant the same outcome for her. The same desire. They stared out the window and watched for the eruption's mushroom cloud to expand, as if, only afterward, between them, something definite could be determined.

Go Deejay

He is lying in bed, on his back, his arms stretched over his head. He is performing one of his innumerable and nearly unbearable tics, repeating his interpretation of the bass line of the standard techno beat. He does this a great deal and has catalogued this techno tic as one of his most charming habits.

I face him. I have a headache. I'm tired. I'm ready for him to leave. "Please."

He continues, rolling onto his side, propping himself up on one elbow. The speed and volume increase. He is bobbing his head to the beat of his own creation.

When we met he told me I was going to be the mother of his children. I laughed and flagged down the bartender, said, "Good luck with that."

The first time we fucked, right before he came, he said, "Something's coming for you." I couldn't help myself. I laughed. He says it every time like he's giving me a special gift.

He works as a security guard, takes his job very seriously. After a late shift, he's still wearing his uniform and if I say something dirty he frowns and straightens the hem of his dark polyester shirt. He says, "I'm still in uniform."

I visited him once at the factory where he patrols. I was bored and lazy so I went looking for a sure thing. He spends most of his time in a small booth with a 13" television and an old computer he uses to play Minesweeper and Solitaire. I watched him for a few minutes before I knocked on the glass. His brow was furrowed as he concentrated on which set of cards to move where and why. He takes solitary pursuits seriously. He opened the door and let me in. There was hardly any room for the two of us but we are not large people. We made it work.

I said, "I'm here to play with your nightstick," and wrapped my hand around the wooden nightstick hanging from his belt.

He shifted uncomfortably, said, "That's a standard piece of security equipment. I probably shouldn't use it for anything untoward."

He impressed me with his appropriate use of the word *untoward*. I got turned on and wanted him, really wanted him. That made me uncomfortable because I prefer to have sex with men who don't turn me on.

"We'll have to make do with your other night stick."

He grinned and quickly unbuckled the heavy, gadget-laden belt around his waist. His pants fell to the floor. "I bet you want to suck my night stick," he said.

I decided to become the girl I normally hate. "Why yes I do, officer."

He grabbed me by my hair and pushed me to my knees. I hardly recognized him. The floor was dirty. My knees were bare because I wore a short, slutty skirt. Getting down like that turned me on even more. I'm a compulsive neat freak. He told me he was a vice cop and I was a streetwalker; I was in real big trouble. He told me to open my mouth to make it all better so I did. Later, he turned me around and lifted my shirt, baring my breasts, pressing me against the glass window. When he came, he said, "Something's really coming for you," and I said, "Something's coming for you too," even though I did not want to encourage him. When he kissed me goodbye, he started doing his techno bass line again. It was a relief to remember why I hated him.

The Turn

She waits until the last turn to say what kind of party this will be.

Dinner, yes, with two other couples—the host and hostess and friends they all share. But in the space between two clicks of the turn signal, she says, "Oh," like she almost forgot, and the rest of the sentence lays bare what she's been failing to mention since early last week when the hostess asked in quiet and cautious yet straightforward terms if they'd "be cool" with this thing that she, the good wife and mother, is now telling her husband—as if in passing, as if to say that dinner starts at eight, that their friends don't eat shellfish, that the night will conclude with a game of charades.

"Oh," he says as the information begins to unfold in his brain.

When the light turns green, he turns the wheel, and all the reasons she said yes, they'd be cool with it, slide from one baby seat to the next—the juice box, the sippy cup, the crumpled baggie of Cheerios, the things that remind her of who she is, who she was, and who she sometimes wishes she could be.

So the car rolls on—beneath railroad tracks, past quiet homes with swimming pools and rope swings, through neighborhoods just like hers—until they reach the house where things will change.

She wants him to keep driving. She wants him to turn back. She wants him to say no, that's not us, but then again she doesn't, and when he pulls into the driveway and puts the car in park and says yes—he's cool with it, too—a part of her dies while another blinks nervously to life.

Porch Light

This Monday, before her morning appointment with her therapist where she discussed enabling tendencies, Susan ate spinach salad with slivered almonds, as she did every day. She drove cautiously just minutes before confidently telling her therapist she was carefree. Susan always walked quickly—even uphill—but decided to not talk with her therapist about obsession. At least not yet. She bought new clogs and thought about kissing her next-door neighbor, Tim. Instead, Susan talked to her therapist about her husband, Donny—his grating interest in sports, his strange, new beard.

That evening, after they finished mowing their adjoining lawns, drank a beer over the fence, and listened to Nirvana's *Nevermind* on her screened-in porch—Donny off at a baseball game—Susan kissed Tim. The music reminded her of the irresponsible time in her life that she described as carefree. Back then she obsessed about happiness, but was usually discontented. She enabled a string of boyfriends, enjoyed dysfunction. Back then she wore vintage prom dresses to clubs, drank until she fell over.

Susan kissed her neighbor who seemed to kiss her back, but nonchalantly finished his beer, propped his hands on his knees, pushed open the screen door, and ambled ankle-deep through her lawn onto his without a goodbye. Pretty cricket noises, pulsing fireflies.

The moon and yard sounds took over after Susan clicked off the table lamp. Sitting in the dusky dark she heard a moth's papery wings clobbering the dim porch light. Susan knew she'd talk of stability at her next appointment, of changing attitudes, of the need for a new, monotone wardrobe and a juicer—a juicer with a variety of settings.

Love Letter

That summer we picnicked in parks, in shady spots where we could forget everyone, especially the boys. I stared at your red hair and its daring angles and wished for more time. In mid-afternoons we sat in your attic bedroom, the hottest place in the house, but the only room where we could escape your parents. The wood paneling gave off an odor brown and safe and secret. Profound and moody, we scribbled judgments in our journals in a language we were sure our parents wouldn't understand.

I remember looking out the window at your mother. Her gray hair was pulled into her gardening hat as she rocked her body back and forth to free the stubborn weeds. Although you resisted, she put her arms around you and nuzzled her nose deep within your hair. I pictured myself in her place. I imagined my arms would fit perfectly around you and our united bodies would leave room for no one else.

One week your parents rented a house at the beach where rain fell for seven straight days. Only on the last day as your dad packed up the car did the sun emerge. Inside someone else's house, we played cards endlessly. I didn't care because I was with you. I would wake to find us inches apart and curled in the same shape.

What I remember most from that summer is the storm. Your mother called from work to warn us a storm was coming and to tell us to close all the windows. We told her what she would want to hear and still in our pajamas went back to watching the video we had rented. Something in the air had changed, some chemistry or electricity had been altered. The birds, normally a rowdy chorus in your yard, were silenced. The trees weren't moving their lush green leaves above your mother's garden. We peered out the window to a yellow-green sky that was unfamiliar and frightening. Foolish and arrogant, we wanted to hide and witness at the same time.

We stood in your sunroom as the winds pulled your backyard down around us. The biggest tree split and fell covering half your yard and crushing your mother's patio furniture. We had never seen anything like it. I reached for your hand. You accepted. We waited it out together and alone, not speaking until the danger had passed and the damage had been done. Only then we realized the power was out. Days would pass before it was restored. We explored your street hand-in-hand as the sun appeared. Together we counted fallen trees and sidestepped downed power lines. Uncertain and happy, we walked through a new world.

HIM

Limp

I grew a flower, an orchid. Pretty color. A little lazy, this flower, hanging toward the ground like it might sniff out more water, but a nice flower.

She didn't say pretty when I gave it to her. She didn't say lazy either. Limp. That's what she said.

I gave her the poem after the flower. And then candy. Unoriginal, cheap. A stuffed animal holding a ridiculous stuffed heart big as my fist.

The flower was the prize. The rest was garnish, afterthoughts, something you only think about when it's standing. Right in front of you.

Almost Ivory

Kathleen Appleby sat on a swing strung between elms. In third grade, Kathleen and he had been the hot couple, kissing after four-square or in the hall while they read books too difficult for their classmates. He hadn't kissed a girl since. The birthmark on her cheek had meant something different to him each time. A tiny hand, a web, a heart with valves and veins.

Kathleen watched him watching her. *What happened to you?* Maybe they both had such thoughts. A graduation party. They'd seen each other here and there since, but the world had gotten so much bigger—and so had he. It had begun in fourth grade. If he had sat beside her, the trees would've collapsed in on them.

Kathleen Appleby. Drunk, alone. That said a lot in a party of drunk boys.

"Do I smell?" she asked. He came closer, against one of the trees. Luckily, it didn't topple over when he leaned against it. He still remembered her smell—and he guessed that was part of the loneliness that happened from peaking at third grade. Ivory. 99.44% pure.

"Yes," he said. "Like old beer."

"I remember you. You were like a stick figure then."

Fourth grade to seventh grade didn't exist for him. Just black. Third grade lacked details, an ethereal glow like the way comic book illustrators drew auras. Kathleen's hair had gotten strung out like a witch's. Her face, hard and pointy. *What had happened to them?* The world had happened to them. Stupid but true.

"Boy, did I love you," she said. "So smart. And the books you read. Stephen King. Very mature. You know, you turned me on to reading. Really."

And look where it got you.

"Hey, would you want to, you know, fuck me?" she said. "No fooling. I mean it. You want to?"

"Yeah, I want to."

"Good. Let's, uh, you know, go somewhere."

They went behind the tree. She asked if he had protection. He said yes, right here, in case he ever should meet Kathleen Appleby again and she wanted to fuck him. Kathleen laughed. Lucky for Kathleen, he'd masturbated like twice already that day, so he wouldn't come right away.

Third grade came into focus, as she was rubbing herself to get ready. He wondered if he should be doing that. How he'd loved Kathleen Appleby, how extra bright the recess world had seemed, that red ball against the black macadam, the white squares drawn in the brightest chalk. He'd forgotten the rich details of that world—about the pop-a-matic Trouble game they'd played during rainy days, of *Electric Company* and Letter Man, who could change words, like *hard* into *lard*.

Kathleen hummed "I'm Leaving on a Jet Plane." It sounded so close to the way Miss Acri had sung it, he and Kathleen knee-to-knee, and it all came back to him, as if it had really happened.

Life Without Operas

My name is ***** ****** and I am lost. A group of big men took my wallet. They gave me a pamphlet, fake tickets to some silly opera, promises to bring binoculars and a cape. They took one of our women.

My name is ***** ****** and nobody's saving much of anybody else. Strength is determined by how well you take your loneliness so if you want to be a poet you're going to have to really look like an asshole. I take pride in the camouflage of my job. You do or will, too.

My name is ***** ****** and today I drew a skeleton with a headset on it making deals even after death and everybody just laughed. For a few panic-filled seconds my boss just stared at the picture. I thought I was about to be fired but instead he called me a fucker and I went to lunch.

My name is ***** ****** and I'm still sore about that money. I hate that eating groceries makes me have less. I hate putting quarters in the washer and dryer. If I knew how to make differences in my life, who knows, maybe she would have been the one. I'd heard of boyfriends selling their girlfriends into prostitution, but just taking someone like that? I'd never seen that opera.

Grover Cleveland Has It Out with America On The Eve Of His Second Inauguration

America, I am feeling vulnerable tonight. I am bright gold foil over melted chocolate. I am the moon made of mercury, cinnamon, and asbestos. I am more machine than man but my heart, my heart is soft as nougat and sad as the end of seasons.

Look, America. We have to talk. The elephant in the room, the one that's—and isn't it just like metaphors that it really does work out to be a sort of elephant this time? Shitting all over the floor of my presidential achievements? You know what I mean, America. You know the hurt surging up and over me, neon-green-and-purple through me, like I'd laid hands on one of those stupid lightning globes they sell at Spencer Gifts.

Benjamin Assface Harrison.

Oh, no, don't worry, America. I'm sure you had your reasons. After all, his grandfather did such an awesome job as president. Dying of pneumonia a few months in counts as doing an awesome job as president, right? (O Harrison the Elder, O fragile, fleeting, lace-hearted president. This world was never meant for one as beautiful as you.)

And now you want me back? An old fat man with pancake jowls and sausage fingers and the heart of a middle manager? My fealty is not forever, my dreams not made for you to smash like Play-Doh on the White House lawn. I am too fond, too fond for my own good and it shines in my eyes, bright pride like small hammers.

Oh, America. WTF, as Thomas Jefferson would have said. This country is a bowl of dick—yet, I feel such love for you. You have a young bright spirit, lit in you like newborn stars, like fireflies over flame. I expect great things of you. Your future is a Mad Lib: you can be brave and foolish and cruel and clean and kind and murderous and hopeful and yes, even sexy. You can be anything you want to be, America.

I am ready to lead. I am ready to follow. I am ready. Deliver me your hopes like crisp white linen, and together we will drive tomorrow out of the bushes and into our strong and waiting arms.

Jerry's Life As Sung To "I Think We're Alone Now"

Children behave. "Will you relax, Deanna, so what if the kid breaks a few things?" dad would say. Mom often looked like the last Kleenex in the box and no one was going to use her and throw her away. Her favorite expression: Be on your toes. I was on my toes, I suppose. Up for school. Hardly ever "sassy" when told to take out the garbage. When she died I learned that she had been on her toes for seventy-seven years. Her feet were damn tired. I never got her a pillow.

That's what they say when we're together. When I met Jeff, I had already come out to my parents. Jeff hadn't. He'd say, "They think that gay people are poison. We emit killing fumes." His family figured us out—we weren't "buddies." His mother remains cold but sends me Christmas cards with messages like "Remember Jesus's birthday. He remembers yours." His father thinks of me as another channel to change. I don't think they fear poison. Is this progress?

And watch how you play. I knew I was gay young. It's like I was a contestant on *You Bet Your Life* and the secret word, Gay, came down and yes, Groucho, that's me. I've felt watched all my life. I met my first lover, Ben, at Polk Junior High School. We could do anything we wanted provided we said "We're not gay. We don't love each other. Only gay people can love each other." That freed us to do what he called "the snooky ookums." Watched. By parents. Neighbors. School. I've spent decades dislodging eyes from my skin. Eyes in my most private places.

They don't understand. Ben and I were "gross, weird, sinful, and only kooks do that kind of thing."

And so we're runnin' just as fast as we can. I ran and ran but they kept moving the finish line. After two and a half decades I realized that the finish line was in their heads, not mine. I stopped running. Even now, so many keep running, faster, faster—how do they do it? Bare feet. Gravel.

Holdin' on to one another's hand. Jeff's hand is my favorite part of his body. I don't rank his parts, but his hand is tops. When I hold it, deep blue forget-me-nots cover the most barren ground inside me. His hand is a map of wisdom. I don't read maps well, but I never feel lost as long as I have his hand.

Tryin' to get away into the night. My friend Mitch tried to get away for years. Booze, drugs, a bunch of guys he slathered all over his body. He quit trying. I was a pallbearer at his funeral. How easily it could have been me in the box. Mitch wore out from the daily battering ram of hate.

And then you put your arms around me and you say I think we're alone now. Alone is a rake standing by the garage door. It needs to be put to good use. Alone is sitting with Jeff watching *My Three Sons,* not saying anything, but knowing when he will laugh at Bub. Alone is being in a crowded mall and trying to start a conversation with a clerk. Alone is finding a place to hide, you think no one will ever find you, you're OK with that, kind of, but someone does find you. Hides with you. And emerges with you. Into light. And darkness.

Dog Beach

He sits out there in his rowboat, mouth half open, the Chicago skyline rising and falling behind him. I walk on my knees though the water. Inching closer, slipping farther out into the lake. There is garbage floating near the surface. Bubble wrap and empty plastic sleeves of crackers. I skirt around them, or try to. I want it to seem like an accident. Like I just drifted over, and then all of a sudden I am next to him and I can say oh, hey, how's it going out here?

He is the lifeguard. Young and bored, probably Mexican, with smooth black hair and sunglasses that reflect the blue sheen of the lake. He wears a standard issue red tank top and his teeth are as white as forever. I am old. And fat, and I have the face of someone who has sustained some kind of injury, only I have not. It is just my face. My nipples are the size of coasters and I have no hair on my chest. He is very young. Possibly eighteen. That would be good, actually. But he is probably younger. I can feel the blood moving through my body when I look at him, even though the water is cold.

"Sir!" he calls out to me. I stare back at the shore and pretend not to hear, ashamed at being noticed. It is crowded here today. It seems like there are a thousand dogs on the beach, wrestling and shitting and chasing wet tennis balls.

"Sir," he says again. I can hear his oars cutting through the lake as he moves closer. "You really shouldn't be out here if you don't have a dog." He points to the beach next to us, the one for people. "It's much cleaner over there." His voice is as dull as an old knife. I can tell that he hates this job, which seems strange to me. I would imagine that sitting in a boat all day would be one of the most relaxing ways to make a dollar.

"I have a dog," I say. "He's over .there." I point vaguely towards the shore. "A German Shepherd," I add, hoping that this will impress him. "His name is Larry."

He looks off into the distance like he is thinking about something very important. He wipes sweat off of his upper lip. I feel something crumple under my toes and pray that it is not a diaper. I do not own a German Shepherd. I do not own any dog at all. I just like this beach because people are friendlier here. I can stand in the sand at the edge of the water, watching the dogs run in and out, back and forth along the shore. People talk to me like we are all in a club together, like I am part of something bigger.

"Alright," he says, starting to back paddle. His arms are skinny and brown, but they look strong, and they make me think about pretending to drown.

Give Me License

I told her that's it on a Thursday, dreading the weekend. I'd asked her to move in and saw the no on her face before she said it. Wanted to smell her in my bed, fuck her first thing in the morning, have her come along to gigs, let the guys in the band see how she looked at me. I sung some but never felt good about it unless she was in the crowd.

I slammed the truck door and drove it away like it was her, pushing it farther and farther, not knowing where I'd end up.

Speeding toward anywhere else, twenty-seven years old, I was leaving her after six years, a death.

I read corny license plates as a strategy to keep from turning around, heading right back and having her open her door, eyes blue and relieved.

DOGKISS

My mom had called it puppy love when I'd first brought her home. "Ron, that's a crush, not love." I thought maybe she was right, wanted her to be.

DRTYGRL

Three years into our relationship, hotel pool. Weekend getaway to Atlantic City. A few games, lots of sex, a comped room from my cousin's bachelor party. Our bodies dripping wet, skin stinking of chlorine and water-logged chests. She turned to me, wine-drunk and make-up-smeared and said she liked it when I got her from behind, had always felt too shy to say it. I immediately pulled her into the sauna room, turned her toward the wall, yanked down her bikini bottom and stuck it in. She whimpered and came in minutes, or pretended to, and I felt like a superhero.

MOMYUV4

She got pregnant two years in. We got used to the idea, but hadn't told anyone when she lost it. Two weeks after the miscarriage she held her sister's baby. I saw the light leave her eyes, saw her watching the ghost of our baby floating away like October leaves trailing the truck.

RUNR4EVR

She always said she was more athletic than me and then giggled. One flexible girl, a gymnast as a kid, a part-time fitness trainer as an adult. I'd get hard watching her stretch. I did insurance work by day, was a drummer at night. My dad liked to tell his friends I'd always banged on things. I liked making empty things into something. And I liked security, getting it for people and having some myself.

FLYINHI

Her one fear was heights. I coaxed her onto the Ferris wheel to help her conquer it. She said it wasn't so much about the fear of falling. It was the way things got smaller and smaller and out of her control. *Like our baby.*

She'd said let's wait. She wanted the freedom to love me with no pressure of what should be. Maybe she'd be childless. Maybe we'd be marriageless. I told her maybe my mother had been right, to jab her where it hurts.

I told her she was chickenshit and that she could balance-beam her ass to some other prick who'd settle for that.

Her eyes, like watery wombs with dead-blue babies, pleaded. I was breaking her again, in a different way.

FREEBYRDZ

The truck coughed. I opened the windows, turned up Pearl Jam on the radio, listened to the wicked drums. Out loud, to the air rushing in, I said, "You're free."

What Is Best In Life?

Amy was this girlfriend I had for a little while. She had frizzy caramelly hair and since I only knew her in the summer all I remember her in were these printed tank tops when all of the other girls wore solid ones. It was like she was saying screw y'all, deal with my tiny stars and anchors. I liked that.

Amy had this thing. I guess she had a few things. Her mom was dead and her aunt lived with her and her dad—they're fuckbuddies, she told me the first time we met. Amy had this little boy Sam who her aunt watched while she was at school or at work. Her dad had a bug up his ass about how Amy had to earn money to take care of Sam even though it would've made more sense and money for her aunt to work, she was an accountant or something. But the aunt stayed home and Amy worked at AirBrush Tees and I went to see her on my breaks.

The thing I mean started not long after we met. We were eating in the food court and figuring out what assholes we both knew when Amy got up and told me to follow her! We went to Kaufmann's, and into the men's room. "Too many ladies in the ladies' room," she said. We went into a stall and I was trying to figure out whether to hang on to her or the wall. "One on each," Amy said, and she was right. After we were done and I was leaning there on the toilet trying to catch my breath, she reached into her shirt and pulled out a Sharpie. She shook it a few times, took the cap off, and wrote CONAN THE BARBARIAN on the door.

"Holy shit," I said, "that's you?" Because you couldn't live in Albany without seeing CONAN THE BARBARIAN on the wall in the can. By that time, CONAN THE BARBARIAN was a better friend to me than Amy. CONAN THE BARBARIAN had been in the boys' room in eighth grade, when I hid from Mr. Drew after cheating on a test. He'd been in the men's room at the grocery store when I had alcohol poisoning before the Spring Dance. He was in the stall at the bar where Kevin and I had tried getting served because Scott told us the owners were cool. I'd even seen CONAN THE BARBARIAN at the Schuyler rest stop when I drove to Syracuse on the Thruway.

Amy just laughed and put the Sharpie back in her shirt. She knew I was hooked, but she knew it was more CONAN THE BARBARIAN than anything. I loved how the marker squeaked on the door, and how its headache smell made me more dizzy. But I couldn't help it. "Why CONAN?" I'd ask. "Why capital letters? Why the different colors?" These days, I know she'd seen and heard it all before. The only thing new to Amy was going home and having her aunt be all you watch Sam, I'm going to the store.

All the dumb questions I asked. God. "Are you the only girl with a Sharpie?" The day after that, I walked into the bathroom at Service Merchandise. She was doing this guy from Record Town. I washed my hands, and I left when I heard the marker rattle.

Hard

I like how Katie's big brown eyes change when she sees me walking toward her checkout line. Like I'm feral and she's not sure if she wants to run scared or tame me.

I put my can of Red Bull on the conveyor belt. She looks at my wet hair and says it must be a pretty awful day to be out collecting the carriages. I shrug and wipe my hand across my head and say it's not that bad. I watch her long fingers wrap around the Red Bull. I watch her lips as she tells me the price. I tell her I'm working at my dad's junkyard tonight, I'll be lonely. She should come visit me.

I doubt she'll show. I sit on a grimy mattress covered with wadded up chip bags and empty beer cans, and play Grand Theft Auto. Her bitchy friends think I'm a loser. I go to the Voc school, like my dad. My mom died when I was twelve. Her mom probably won't let her come. Still, I imagine Katie lying next to me and I'm just starting to jerk off when the dog barks and my phone buzzes with Katie's text. I stuff myself back in my pants, make sure the dog is tied up tight and walk down the gravel driveway.

Katie's waiting at the gate in the fence. The rain's stopped and under the streetlight, fog rises around her like a giant halo. I reach the chain link and stare out at her. She smells like apples and lemon. She looks so small without her smock.

"You came," I say.

"I'm here."

"Your friends didn't talk you out of it?"

"I didn't tell them."

"I'm impressed." I wonder if she told her mother. I don't ask.

"I brought some homemade chocolate chip cookies," she says. She lifts up her hand and shows me a bag. "Are you going to let me in?"

I pull the key from my pocket and unlock the gate. She steps into the yard and the gate clangs closed behind us. I snap the lock and grab the bag.

63

We walk up to the house, and I take her hand and lead her through the office that stinks like grease, and into the back room. I brush off a spot on the mattress, and she sits with her back against the wall. I flop down next to her and feel her arm warm against mine. I don't say anything. I eat all the cookies. She doesn't complain.

I crumple the bag and throw it across the room, then turn and kiss her. She tastes like toothpaste. I'm surprised how hard she kisses me back. I reach under her shirt, unhook her bra. I squeeze her breasts. She whimpers like she's surprised. I take her hand and put it over my dick. I tell her how hard she's made me. I unzip my fly.

"Take it out," I say. She hesitates. I do it myself. "I need you," I whisper.

I lie back with my arms behind my head and close my eyes. She grips me with those long fingers and takes me in her mouth. She doesn't know what to do. It hits me that she never did this before. I can't hold back. I come like a baby crying.

I lie there, panting, afraid to open my eyes. I know Katie is kneeling there, looking down at me with her big eyes. I don't want to know if she's laughing. I don't want to know if she's crying.

And The One Guy Turns To The Other And Says, "I'll Trade You Mine For Yours"

The mechanic works on cars driven by rich people, people with built-in swimming pools and summer houses at Harvey's Lake. One of his regulars—a lawyer with his own TV commercial—comes in and tells tell him jokes, lewd, shitty jokes about the black guy and the Jew and the Polack sitting at a bar, and they sit there, the mechanic and the rich guy, and they bullshit about guy things.

The lawyer rolls up his sleeves and tucks his tie in and he smiles at the mechanic because he admires him, he thinks he likes the grease stains splattered all over the mechanic's t-shirt and the thickness of his fingers. He knows stuff, knows it in a confident, easy way that the lawyer never could. The lawyer envies the easy way the mechanic moves around the shop, picking up large tools and prying under his Saab, twisting and pulling and massaging parts of it that the lawyer never even knew were there, and that makes the lawyer think of his wife, rolling away from him in their king-sized bed each morning, her brown tousled hair covering her soft face. Ever hear the one about the lawyer whose wife was banging the postman?

The mechanic's got forty-five minutes left in his shift and then he's got to rotate his girlfriend's tires and change the oil before driving her car home. She's four months along, but she still goes to the bars to watch him shoot darts, drinking orange juice in a short glass so it looks like a screwdriver. Some dick called her fat last week and the mechanic punched him in the nose, spurting blood all over the carpet and busting open his own hand. He got dragged out of the place yelling and the Eagles lost and when his girlfriend came out she was crying, her mascara running all down her cheeks, and he couldn't figure out why until she grabbed her stomach, saying You did this to me. I wanted to be a model.

The lawyer decides he won't tip the mechanic. He's probably ripping him off anyway, charging him all that for labor. The lawyer dreads going back to the office to work on his case—a round, snippy woman who slipped on spilled soup in Safeway and bellyaches of a ruined back. He hates the woman, but he knows he'll win the case for her. He hates most of his clients—middle-aged divorcees who throw themselves at him, lazy men who scream malpractice, rich teenagers who need to wiggle out from under their DUIs. He tells the mechanic one more joke—one last story that he picked up from a client during their last meeting—and is grateful when the guy laughs.

And the mechanic feels bad for the rich guy, who has a Michael Bolton CD tucked between the seats and a silver disco ball hanging from the rearview mirror. He sees the rich guy's commercial a lot watching People's Court during his lunch break—the sad little jingle trying to sound like a rap, the rich guy's shiny dark hair perfectly parted on the left as he talks about his success rate—and he knows he'd never be able to afford him. The rich guy is talking loud, embellishing his joke, but the mechanic can't seem to pay attention, he's staring at the clock, counting the minutes that come like sharpened darts headed for the bull's eye, and the only thing he remembers after the guy leaves is the punch line.

Sniffing Out The Boundaries

Jen stands by the chain link fence in a red hat knitted in the pattern of a strawberry. Snowflakes tick the hedges. I walk past the soccer boys and hopscotch girls and lean on the fence beside Jen. She frowns. I kiss her cheek. A quick peck, like the one last night, in the alley, but quicker. She rubs her cheek. Her face flushes to match her hat. She punches my arm. I fake-punch her face. My fist stops an inch from her nose. The bell rings. She hikes her pink backpack over her shoulder and walks across the gravel playground. I catch up and walk beside her, not so close anyone would notice and not so far I can't smell her shampoo.

One More Thing I Didn't Do

Someone else's backyard. The pool, a cement square holding warm blue water. The homeowner, Angie, was a college friend of my wife's. Nobody knew the husband, Angie's third, a guy named Doug with big naked muscles and a brogue. He slouched in a deck chair and scowled at the pool.

"It's going green."

Water this warm, he told us, the algae takes over. You get a swamp. The water temperature was set at eighty, same as the air. Mid-August in Vancouver. The kids—our one and Angie's two—liked the water warm. Everyone did, except Doug.

To cross the border we'd idled in a two-hour line of cars. The border guard was a stout man with a full white beard. Santa in a booth. He said, "What is your relationship to these people?"

At a Petro Canada , I asked for Marlboros. The clerk, a strong teen with cheeks like peeled plums, flipped me a red pack called du Maurier. I stood outside and smoked two to equal one.

In the car, my wife said, "Look, are you going to watch him? This weekend he's your job."

"Look at that speed limit," I said. "We can go ninety."

Angie had Monica, eleven, and Rory, six. Our Teddy was five. Rory could swim, but not Teddy, and Angie made them both wear life jackets. Gangly Monica wore a ball cap, a Canucks t-shirt, and glossy black shorts past her knees. Without warning she threw off her cap and dove in.

Angie and my wife were sitting at an umbrella table. They were huddled close, faces to the sun, backs to the pool. Angie reached into her bathing suit and removed two flesh-colored bra cups. "I'm wearing falsies," she said. She put them on the table, humps up. My wife ran her fingers over the rounded surfaces.

Doug was hosing down the bright yard. The lawn and the flowers were very much alive. Back in Tacoma, the grass behind our apartment was dead. So, for the record: my wife and Angie, sitting together, backs to the pool. Doug in the grass. Me, off by myself, in a chair facing the pool, trying to suck nicotine out of a du Maurier.

"Hey," I said. I saw a head, alone, bobbing. I got up and went to the deep end. It was Teddy. His face was calmly falling under and then rising. I watched this happen three times. I stood there, blew smoke.

Like a shot Doug was in the pool. He grabbed Teddy, raised him up, and set him on the concrete. Teddy was stunned. "Wow," he said. He wasn't wearing a life jacket.

My wife and Angie were twisted around. "Honey, where's your life jacket?" Angie said.

"What happened?" my wife said.

"He was playing," I said. I caught Doug's eye.

"He wasn't playing," Doug said.

"I hate the life jacket." Teddy started weeping.

"Honey, you have to wear it," Angie said, and she got up.

My wife gave me a look. "You watch him."

After dark my wife and Angie sat outside swigging Chablis, cackling. I was upstairs in Rory's room, lying on a choo-choo-train bed, next to the boys in sleeping bags.

On the way home, my wife turned to me. "You know what Angie said? She said she knows he'd save her. He would rescue her. She knows."

I was in no mood. "What's Angie doing in another country?"

"She has Doug. She has a house, a pool."

"I'm just saying this isn't us. This is other people."

My wife turned away. She laughed once. She started talking out the window.

Beasts And Men

The foreman curses the chilled rain, the gunmetal clouds. It's the day before Thanksgiving, and Joe's crew is calling it quits an hour after lunch. They wrap cords, gather tools. The men grumble—their paychecks will be light this week.

Dodging raindrops and puddles, they enter the bar. The first pitchers disappear quickly. Refills arrive, a tray of shots. Joe and his workmates rack up games of eight ball, and pleasing, the bones-and-gut thump of each break. Their clothes stink of the damp and cold. The high school teachers arrive at three, the office drones at five-fifteen. The bartender switches on the Christmas lights, an orderly galaxy circling the bar. In the flickering stillness, Joe recalls the Christmas tree in his childhood home. His mother is dead; his father gone south. The moment fades. The bar erupts in rejoined conversations.

The cigarette haze thickens. Joe's group dwindles to a dangerous few, Stu Geeseman and the Waller brothers, hard men familiar with the county jail and the local meth scene. In the cramped bathroom, Joe takes a snort. The gritty clump tattoos him from hairline to jaw. The walls' crude graffiti blurs. Joe's heart grinds in protest. He has no plans, not for tonight, not for tomorrow. The present stretches to the horizon, and he is dwarfed by the emptiness. Stu lifts another mound to Joe's nose.

They return to their table to find it claimed by a clique of secretaries, chatty women who sip blender drinks and wear sensible shoes. The powders' dubious chemistry electrifies Joe's veins. A song he remembers from his teenage years plays on the juke. His machine parts—the sprockets, cogs, and pumps—smolder beneath his skin. He orders a beer. He tries to sing along with the juke, but he is out of sync. The harried bartender brings both his beer and a shot he didn't ask for. Joe lifts the shot glass to eye-level, his gaze lost in the clear liquid.

Hours later, Joe stands behind the house he once shared with the woman he loved. The rain has not let up. Hazy mathematics have emptied his wallet. He can't go home, his apartment's walls too bare, too white. The neighbor's shepherd rattles his chain. Joe recalls the dog as a pup. "Yes," he told the woman he loved. "We can get a dog too if you'd like."

Shivering and soaked, he stands at a spot he once ringed with paper lanterns. He steps closer, ducking beneath the maple's low branches, his footsteps hushed by mud and tanbark and blood-red leaves. A forgotten bucket rests beside the picnic table. Notions of accidents and omens blur. He turns over the bucket. Leaf-speckled water splashes around his boots. He steps onto the bucket, grabs a hold of the window ledge and peeks inside. On the kitchen counter, a turkey pan, cut flowers in a vase. Rivulets snake across the pane, the scene a still-life precisely lit, once-familiar surroundings blurred by tearing glass and fading memories. The dog he bought her trots into the kitchen.

The dog, no longer a pup, cocks its white-curled head. The tiny thing begins to yelp: insistent, high-pitched, piercing. Joe places a hand upon the glass. The vibrations seep into his palm. The aroused shepherd joins in, his ears perked, his barks threatening and deep. Twice, the shepherd chokes himself with chain-rattling lunges. Joe, in his moment of want and need, howls, too. Here is the chorus of beasts and men.

The Taster's Last Meal

When I first began tutoring Shin Chan-Hwan, I did not feel attracted to him. I found his shy sadness endearing, but his body repulsed me. He had the narrow bones and taut sinews of an unhealthy woman, and yet his face betrayed masculinity. I found this combination grotesque, perhaps because I did not yet know of my preference for it.

The Supreme Leader appointed Shin Taster of Meals because He believed nobody would feed poison to such a sympathetic figure. Shin was orphaned at ten when his mother, a prostitute, was killed by one of our Dear Leader's bodyguards. He was raised by the Generalissimo and His staff. I volunteered out of pity to tutor him, convincing the Generalissimo that the more worldly Shin became, the better able to notice culinary oddities he would be.

While it was the boy's mitochondrial response that mattered most to the Dear Leader, He could see the benefits of having one taster for as long as possible: familiarity with His favorite dishes, a well-practiced nose, and the social ease that comes with not having a stranger at the table.

Not long after we met, Shin introduced me to sexual passion. Although I taught him to read and to know his food, we figured out as peers how two men might lie together, and how, over time, their lust might give way to a stronger bond.

Shin became a national mascot, a symbol of the invincibility of the Democratic People's Republic of North Korea. If some callous usurper should manage to poison Shin *and* the Supreme Leader, the People would never stand for Shin's sacrifice and would revolt immediately.

The General had always believed in a top-down sentimentality, but many of us in the Cabinet knew better. We knew how tenuous was His hold over the Premiers, let alone over the writhing passions of the People. We heard tales of our cousins' cousins in China growing wealthy as we begged for moderate villas in the hills outside Pyongyang. Most worrisome, we watched as the Generalissimo grew both weary and furious—a dangerous combination—over constant criticism from other nations.

Soon, a few of us decided that no consequence of an assassination could be worse for Korea than the inevitable consequences of no assassination.

Because I had tutored Shin for so long, it fell on me to approach him. I insisted we give him the chance to be a knowing martyr, one whom the People would praise long after his demise. Perhaps I felt he deserved the chance to look in my eyes as I condemned him.

"Shin Chan-Hwan," I said as we began a lesson on European mushrooms, "I suspect you have waited for this day." I showed him the vial of thallium, a poison slow enough to wait for the Leader to eat before killing Him and His taster.

I held my gloved fingers to Shin's mouth, to express the risk of discussing the matter further, to indicate the means by which the poison was to be administered, and, finally, to touch his lips before they parted one last time for our Korea.

When I removed my hand, Shin said "Yes, I have waited." His resolve brought tears to my eyes.

I could not watch as Shin tasted the tainted *insam-ju*. I do not know if he omitted his customary sniff of the gingery liquor, or if he took a larger sip than usual to steel himself against the effects the poison would later have. I must believe, though, that as the liquor passed over his lips, he thought not only of his loathing for his keeper, and not only of his country, but also of me.

THEM

Breaking Tradition

Diana waited on the sofa, squeezing her hands into fists then letting them go. She'd sent her boy, Davie, upstairs, so he wouldn't be there when his father got home.

It had been an accident, what Davie had done. He was trying to help by setting the table. He had stretched to place a folk down on the opposite side, and his body snagged the table cloth. One of the wine glasses teetered, then fell against a plate, shattering into a dozen pieces.

It was almost beautiful, this bright, shiny chaos. Except that it was one of Alan's grandmother's crystal glasses, which Alan always hand-washed and carefully returned to the cabinet after each use.

Diana had cleared and reset the table with their plain wine glasses. She laid out only two settings, deciding Davie should eat early and go to his room. Alan's rage was infrequent, but fierce. Last year, she'd been left with a bruise where he'd grabbed her arm, after she accidentally backed her car into his. Later, he cried an apology, and she silently unpacked her suitcase. She told herself then that Davie was the line she would not let him cross.

Alan had loved his grandmother, and these four glasses—now three—were the only things he had left of hers. How the love of one person could lead to the hurting of another made no sense to Diana, but she knew it was how things sometimes were.

She had already opened the wine, but had refrained from drinking, lest she be in a better mood than Alan and tell him too soon, too casually. She waited silently until she heard his car, its particular sound; the closing door, the tick of the engine cooling. Then Alan's steps. She rose, preparing herself for the night.

Alan opened the door with a face somber and still, as though he had already heard the news.

"Hi dear," she said. "Everything ok?"

He nodded, but did not speak. Then, after setting down his things, he asked, as if just being reminded of cordiality, "How was your day?"

"Fine," she said, "fine."

She led him to the dining room, poured the wine, and served dinner. They ate mostly in silence. He asked where Davie was. "Upstairs," she said, refusing to explain, even when he asked again.

They were almost finished the meal when she told him what had happened.

He remained silent; she could not read him.

"Was he hurt?" Alan finally asked.

"No."

Then, after a long pause, he said, "Then don't worry."

"Really?" She could hear the shock in her own voice, the judgment it implied. Alan could turn on that alone.

But he simply nodded and said, "It's not important."

She could not believe it, his lack of anger. She waited for it to appear, subverted and intense, but he remained calm as he finished his food, that patina of solemnity still coating his face.

After she served dessert, a lemon pound cake with blueberries, she asked, "Are you alright?"

He nodded again, but didn't speak. He could not tell her what had happened earlier on the train home. It had broken his heart. A mother and her son, who was about Davie's age, had taken the seat behind him. Alan had barely noticed them except to wonder if they would make much noise, if the boy would push into the back of his seat.

But they were quiet, until the boy said to his mother, in a weak voice, almost a whisper, "I'm breaking."

"You're breaking what?" she asked, annoyed.

"I'm breaking," he said. Nothing else.

The Ballad Of This And That

They met in college at a party. This was drinking beer. That was sipping from a wine cooler. This spotted That through the crowd but didn't want to make the first move. This was shy, but as the night drew on That wandered over toward the corner of the room This was standing in and This couldn't help but blurt out, "You're beautiful."

This paused, looked at That, and said, "You're drunk."

And so it began, as these things often do.

That had just gotten out of a long relationship and wasn't ready yet to date. This understood and said there was no hurry. They talked frequently on the phone or via online chat. Every day that passed This fell more and more in love. That, however, was not ready to start dating again, despite the fact they had already made love multiple times. Right now they were just friends, That explained, friends with benefits, and what harm could come of that?

The semester stretched on, and they began talking less and less. When they did see each other, their lovemaking was hesitant and awkward. Finally That confessed that there was someone else, someone that That had been seeing for a few weeks now. This tried to hold back all the emotions swirling inside but couldn't, they were like a tornado, tearing out every cell and particle inside This's body. This screamed and yelled and picked things up and threw them at the ground and the wall and kicked things and, all at once, calmed down and left.

And so it ended, as these things often do.

Except, many years later, That happened to run into This in one of the largest cities in the world. It was one of those coincidences that couldn't be anything other than fate.

"How have you been?" That asked.

This shrugged. "I've been fine. You?"

"No complaints."

There was a silence, and That wanted to tell This about the past couple years, all the missteps and mistakes, all the times That had thought about This and wanted to call or text or e-mail but had always been too scared, too chickenshit, to take that next step.

"So," This said.

That nodded. "So."

"It was good seeing you."

"Was it?"

This nodded but there was nothing in This's expression that said this was true. This said goodbye and stepped around That but That stepped with This, almost like it was choreographed, the two suddenly paired up in a dance, both just standing still then, staring at the other, waiting for the music to start.

Locked

The lock failed. It locked itself unbidden. It was the door's fault, but Tim worried that maybe someone, God even, felt that he and Linda had failed at something unknowable; that the locked door was being offered up as a metaphor for their relationship even. They kept trying to reach each other, to reach out? To be better? And yet they kept falling away from each other? Something like that, maybe?

Earlier in the day, they had taken their child to church for the first time. Mike was nearly four and excited about church because he didn't know what to expect. It was an adventure. It was UU and so nothing too intense or Jesus-y. Just some songs and talk about cooperative farming.

Linda thought it was just right but Tim missed the drama. There was no body and no blood. No incense. No stations of the cross. There was no sense of fear and no opportunity for redemption.

The music had been nice enough, as had the volunteer in charge of membership they'd spoken to afterward. "Here," he told them as they stood in the entry of the church, the April air whistling in through the cracks in the old building, "you will be responsible for finding your own spiritual path."

What he wanted was less responsibility for his spiritual path and not more. He wanted someone to say, this is what you should do and then everything will be okay. He wanted the reassurance a child wants: that his family will always go on as they are; One hand in one hand in one hand.

He thought of his own father, taking Tim and his sisters to a candlelight Mass in a small wooden church filled with believers. He remembered the cold air and the way the candle shook in his hand dripping wax onto its paper container. Later, when the candles were blown out and the lights turned back on, all of the magic was gone and they were just people in a cold building waiting for the night to end. And now he was behind the locked door in the garage, barred from entry. He felt as small as a child waiting to be let in. Smaller than his small son even, as he glimpsed the sliver of light flickering from beneath the door.

Waffles and Honey

I walk in the bicycle lane with your voice. Traffic in my left ear chops and screws part of your sentences. I don't care if I can't understand part of what you say; you are a taut ribbon.

I'm working for the day I lumber through the door and you are sitting on the couch, eraser in your mouth, and you cock your head toward me and ask how my day was, where I don't have to walk with traffic just to have an excuse to hear you.

Circling The Flame

A moth circled the loose light bulb that plunged a pregnancy of light down on them from his low ceiling. They sat on the narrow couch pretending to watch a shitty movie that was blathering on in front of them. They remained silent and compressed.

He had the powerful urge to just go for it. He saw himself fondle her breasts and whisper something sexy into her ears, like the guy in this despicable romantic non-comedy of a film he'd rented. What the hell was he thinking?

She stared at her hands and thought of his forehead that turned into an accordion whenever he smiled or frowned. He was a hell of a vision. She was getting hot and not in a good way under the down blanket wrapped around her sweaty thighs. She'd told him she was freezing so she could hide the burger and fries that had salt-saturated her into a bloat float. She was ready to moo like the cow that she was. Why didn't she just order a damn salad? That's what you were supposed to do on dates.

She knew what he expected. Sex. So, why not? They'd already been going out for a week. What the hell was she saving herself for?

He was afraid that if he went for it she would haul off and smack him and then what? One minute he had a girlfriend in his apartment with smoldering hips, who actually appeared to like him, and the next she'd be running for the door screeching all sorts of names at him like the lustmonger he was–a sloppy dog in heat. He hadn't had sex in too many goddamn moons to count. Maybe he should just wait another week, continue to masturbate to basically anything that ran through his head or didn't.

Could she bear to sleep alone again tonight? How many nights had she blanked out to her TiVo-d programs, Oprah and Dancing With the Stars, scarfing down the remains of an after work drive-through raid at McDonalds? She watched the moth for a while as it shuddered around the light and then turned to him. His accordion forehead stretched his face into a smile. Might have been creepy or sweet, she couldn't tell. She let the damp comforter slip to the rug. She realized that there was no other way to reply.

The Breaking Heart of God

They asked and besought him: 'Lord, show us the secrets of the Heaven.' But Jesus answered: "I can reveal nothing to you before I have put off this body of flesh."
—The Gospel of Bartholomew

He held her trembling head in his hands like a rotten melon, trying his best to accept those tremors for himself. He wanted to help her along, through this thing, but couldn't speak yet. A full moon of terror and swell, her brown eyes lost in her pasty flesh, a grotesque masque of the face whose lines he had traced with his tongue and lips—it burdened him to look at her, but he forced himself to, because that's what love was for him—the immediacy of facing this other person and what they brought with them, the sad facts of their life and their unequal happinesses, and knowing they would do the same for you, no matter what the cost, no matter the distance. And for Frank and Shirlee, the cost had been great—children, health, their marriage—and the return non-existent. Yet twenty years after their divorce, he remained at her side. She called; he came.

Shirlee had been with him during years he could no longer remember except to know they had passed, when he noticed his guts sagging under his flesh, the penis disappeared into a rat of hair between his legs, the gray in her temples spreading like sea-spray on the blackness of her head. She could still whisper in his ear, and poked him when she wanted him to bend forward so he could hear her breathily rattle her words into his ear.

Now. Frank.

No.

I'm tired, Frank.

Go to sleep then.

Read to me, Frank.

He checked her intravenous fluids, filled the hypodermic, tears blooming, and read:

And he led them to a place called Cherubim, that is, the place of truth. And he beckoned to the angels of the West. And the earth was rolled up like a papyrus, and the abyss was exposed to their eyes. When the apostles saw it, they fell on their faces. But Jesus said to them: "Did I not say to you it was not good for you to see the abyss?" And he again beckoned to the angels, and the abyss was covered up.

Frank drew her limp body into his arms and tears came, and he cursed God. Over and over, he promised things he had no power over, cursed, and over and over again cursed. When he had purged, when her cooling body forced his fear of what he had done to surface, his only consoling thought was that tender thing he had learned in Sunday School, so long ago, that when a person died, when Shirlee died from the chemical he'd injected to force the issue—God's temple, God's body, after all—of all the hearts in the world and all the cherubim and seraphim and doctors and nurses and police who would soon pass judgement, God's heart was the first to break.

Lies

She said I wonder if our daughter is telling us the truth. *He said* probably not—every body lies. *She said* but don't you want to know when and if they will arrive? *He said* hard to know anything. *She said* or if her husband will be with her? *He said* her husband began lying before it became the national norm. *She said* it complicates my grocery shopping. *He said* so we can lie to them. *She said* like what? *He said* we could pretend your brother didn't tell us about the restraining order. *She said* that's not a lie, it's an omission. *He said* so forget "pretend." *She said* does "imagine" fit in? *He said* remember that old *New Yorker* cartoon of a file cabinet with drawers labeled "Our Facts" "Their Facts" "Neutral Facts" "Disputable Facts" *She said* like "True Facts" and "False Facts." *He said* now only one label is necessary. *She said* like what? *He said* "Lies." We'll tell whoever shows up that we got the dates wrong. *She said* it's hard to get dates wrong. *He said* like where and when. *She said* meaning what? *He said* like where you were last Monday. *She said* I already told you where I was last Monday. Do you want me to say it again? *He said* no, once is enough for any lie.

Emergency

02-14-12: Patient presents complaining of sporadic chest fibrillations and recent bouts of insomnia. Seems otherwise inarticulate; speech reduced to gutteral word spasms. Noted shortness of breath, pupils dilated though reactive. Pulse systolic and arrhythmic. BP was low, 82/50. Family history suggests no heart disease or disorders. Healthy diet, moderate exercise. Further examination impeded by patient's sudden hysteria—refusal to disrobe or uncross arms, lashing out, hissing, etc. Restraints finally applied. Subsequent physical exam revealed a small cell phone, embedded in the skin over sternum, vibrating. Upon surgical removal a voice emerged: ". . . but I love you." Psych consult suggested.

Let's Get Together Again Soon

And you can remember your time in France while sipping your Orangina, or laugh and bitch at the troop of contractors you've paid to enlarge your home, or catch the rise of your own emotion thinking of choices you've made for your kids—who do sound great; I look restless, but I am sincere: Ryan—Ryan, is it?—the boy, who's clearly not homosexual, prized as he is by the boys on his team; or Eliana, who seems brilliant, I would agree, though I know you're not trying to say that. We'll do this again. You'll sit with your back to the wall, to the art we ignore but find tasteful. You won't be ready to die for a smoke like you would have when we were in college. You won't remember that one weird day when you gripped the cracking branch with your toes as it broke and we fell in the river. Purity, fitness, your subject will be: of course your kids never watch TV! I will attend. I will smile, and you will smile, and I'll try to be less distracted by the blistering lack of all sexual tension.

Akimbo

We were painting the nursery in the nude. Slapping beige paint over walls the color of a baby's tongue. We'd been at it awhile. The pink kept bleeding through and we didn't use drop cloths because the carpet was going too—this sort of sculpted wall-to-wall that reminded me of my grandmother's house and smelled like cigarettes and corn. So we were manic about it, spattering ourselves, our glasses, our hair and forearms, our privates. You painted a heart on your chest. I painted a swath of it across my forehead. Some Flock of Seagulls song played on the radio. There was this jolt and it made us stop and then another jolt and you said, whoa Nellie. The window glass trembled. Bits of plaster coptered to the floor. The paint can danced. You were trying to come to me and all I could think of was the electric football game me and my brothers had when we were kids and how we'd spend ages setting up our offensive and defensive lines and when we'd finally flip the switch, all the little plastic players would just stand in one place and vibrate impotently. That was you, beautiful and vibrating, your arms akimbo, looking like all you wanted then was to break free, achieve forward momentum, catch me, before the room split apart between us.

Author Biographies

To match pieces with authors, visit www.writenic.com one year after *Stripped*'s release date.

Amber Sparks's work has appeared in various publications, including recently in *Barrelhouse, Wigleaf, trnsfr, PANK, Annalemma, Gargoyle* and *New York Tyrant*. She is the fiction editor at *Emprise Review,* and a contributor at literary blogs Vouched and Big Other. She lives in Washington, DC with a husband and two beasts, and blogs sometimes at www.ambernoellesparks.com. She is currently at work on a novel.

Ashley Inguanta earned her MFA from the University of Central Florida. Most recently, her photography has appeared in *make/shift* magazine. Ashley is also a steady contributing artist for *SmokeLong Quarterly,* and has contributed art to Emerson College's *Redivider. Her fiction and poetry have appeared in SmokeLong Quarterly, Gone Lawn, Pindeldyboz, Elephant Journal, Sweet: A Literary Confection, Breadcrumb Scabs, Wigleaf, and more. She recently earned an Honorable Mention in Glimmer Train for their Very Short Fiction Award.*

Aubrey Hirsch's work has appeared in *Third Coast, Hobart, Whiskey Island, PANK,* and others. She currently lives in Colorado Springs where she is at work on a novel with the support of the Daehler fellowship.

Darlin' Neal is the author of the short story collections, *Rattlesnakes and The Moon* (Press 53, February 2010) and the forthcoming, Elegant Punk (Press 53, 2012). She is the 2011 DH Lawrence Fellow at the Taos Summer Writers Conference. Her stories have appeared in *The Southern Review, Shenandoah, Puerto del*

Sol, Smokelong Quarterly, Eleven Eleven, The Rio Grande Review, The Best of The Web Anthology and dozens of other magazines. Her fiction and nonfiction have been nominated numerous times for the Pushcart Prize. She holds an assistant professorship in the MFA program at The University of Central Florida, and is Fiction Editor of the *Florida Review*. She also serves as faculty advisor to UCF's undergraduate literary arts magazine, The Cypress Dome, and for The Writers in The Sun Reading Series for which she brings in writers of national caliber each semester.

Ellen Parker writes fiction. She is editor of the online literary magazine FRiGG.

Erin Fitzgerald writes, lives, and teaches in western Connecticut. Her stories have appeared in many of her favorite literary journals, and she is happy about that. Find her online at rarelylikable.com.

Ethel Rohan is the author of *Hard to Say*, PANK, 2011 and *Cut Through the Bone*, Dark Sky Books, 2010, the latter named a 2010 Notable Story Collection by The Story Prize. Her work has or will appear in *The Good Men Project*, *The Chattahoochee Review*, *Los Angeles Review*, *Potomac Review* and *Southeast Review Online* among many others. She earned her MFA in fiction from Mills College, California. Raised in Dublin, Ireland, Ethel Rohan is now a resident of San Francisco, California. Visit her at ethelrohan.com.

Gay Degani has published in various anthologies and on-line at *Night Train*, *Monkeybicycle*, *LITnIMAGE*, *Every Day Fiction*, among others. She is co-editor of Flash Fiction Chronicles and an editor at *Smokelong Quarterly*. Her collection of short stories is called *Pomegranate*. Find a list of her work at www.gaydegani.com.

Gill Hoffs is a full time mother and as-often-as-possible writer. When she isn't helping at her son's nursery or cuddling him, she writes books and short stories while consuming her son's weight in chocolate. Her work has won several competitions and is available online and in several anthologies. She lives in England with her scientist husband and son, Angus, and has worked throughout Britain with children with a variety of needs. As a teenager she found a plastic explosive on a Scottish beach and tried to make candles with it, thinking it was wax. Do say hello on Facebook [mentioning *Stripped*] or contact her at: scottishredridinghood@hotmail.com.

Heather Fowler received her M.A. in English and Creative Writing from Hollins University. She has taught composition, literature, and writing-related courses at UCSD, California State University at Stanislaus, and Modesto Junior College. Her work has been published online and in print in the US, England, Australia, and India, and appeared in such venues as *Night Train, Storyglossia, Surreal South, JMWW, Prick of the Spindle, Short Story America* and others, as well as having been nominated for both the storySouth Million Writers Award and Sundress Publications Best of the Net. website: www.heatherfowlerwrites.com

Jeanne Holtzman is an aging hippie, writer and health care practitioner, not necessarily in that order. Her work has appeared in many journals including *Night Train, Blip Magazine, The Los Angeles Review, JMWW, Annalemma, elimae* and *Used Furniture Review* and was longlisted this year for Wigleaf's top 50 very short fictions. You may reach Jeanne at J.holtzman@comcast.net.

Jess Charest was born and raised in the Catskill Mountains of Upstate New York. She is persuing an MFA at Chatham University where her focus is fiction and children's writing. Her chapbook of flash fiction *Bellyful of Nonsense* was released by Wild Planet Press in 2011. She is currently hard at work, watching Shark Week.

Kathy Fish's stories have appeared in *Indiana Review, Mississippi Review* online, *Denver Quarterly, Quick Fiction, Guernica*, FRiGG and elsewhere. She guest edited Dzanc Books' Best of the Web 2010. A chapbook of her work appears in *A PECULIAR FEELING OF RESTLESSNESS: FOUR CHAPBOOKS OF SHORT SHORT FICTION BY FOUR WOMEN* (Rose Metal Press, 2008). Another chapbook, WILD LIFE is forthcoming from Matter Press in 2011 as well as a collection of short stories and flash, TOGETHER WE CAN BURY IT, from Cow Heavy Books.

Kerri D. Schuster is a poet and teacher. She is a member of the Greater Philadelphia Wordshop Studio, and her poem, "Poems Everywhere," won second place in the 2011 Charlotte Miller Simon Poetry Contest.

Kierstin Bridger lives in the San Juan Mountains of western Colorado. She is the 2011 winner of the Mark Fischer Poetry Prize. Kierstin's published works include a micro-fiction piece "Condomnation" in the 2011 issue of the Porter Gulch Review, the one act play "Ruminations in the Median" featured in The University of Washington's literary publication Bricolage. Her short story "Girl's Room," was printed in UW Women's Voices. She has performed her poetry at Sparrows, a well-loved poetry Festival in Salida, Colorado. She has been a featured writer and reader at events such as P-3 (Performance, Poetry & Prose) in Salida and at After Long Silence in Seattle. She has lead Haibun workshops in Salida and Telluride, Colorado.

Meg Tuite's writing has appeared or is forthcoming in numerous journals including *Berkeley Fiction Review, 34th Parallel, One, the Journal, Monkeybicycle, Hawaii Review* and *Boston Literary Magazine*. She is the fiction editor of *The Santa Fe Literary Review* and Connotation Press. Her novel "Domestic Apparition" (2011) is now available through San Francisco Bay Press (www.sanfranciscobaypress.com). She has a monthly column "Exquisite Quartet" up at *Used Furniture Review*. Her blog: http://megtuite.wordpress.com.

Michelle Reale is an academic librarian on faculty at Arcadia University in the suburbs of Philadelphia. Her work has appeared in a variety of publications, including The Pedestal, *Gargoyle*, *PANK*, *JMWW*, *Smokelong Quarterly*, *Staccato*,*Word Riot*, Moon Milk Review and *elimae and others*. Her work was included in Dzanc's 2011 *Best of the Web* Anthology. Her short fiction collection, *Natural Habitat*, was published by Burning River in 2010. Her short fiction chapbook, *Like Lungfish Getting Through the Dry Season* (2011), is available from Thunderclap Press. She has been twice nominated for a Pushcart Prize.

Myfanwy Collins lives and writes on the north shore of Massachusetts. Please visit her at: www.myfanwycollins.com

Nicole Monaghan's work has appeared in *Bartleby Snopes, Foundling Review, Storyglossia, PANK, Used Furniture Review,* and *Literary Mama*, among many other literary journals and in print anthologies. She is the founder and editor of *Nailpolish Stories, a Tiny and Colorful Literary Journal*. Nicole received several awards at both the 61st and 62nd Annual Philadelphia Writers' Conferences including three First Prize Honors (2010) in the categories of Flash Fiction, Literary Short Story, and Memoir. She lives with her husband and three children outside of Philadelphia. Visit her at www.writenic.wordpress.com.

Pamela Painter has written two story collections, the award-winning *Getting to Know the Weather* and *The Long and Short of It,* and is co-author of *What If? Writing Exercises for Fiction Writers*. Her stories have appeared in *The Atlantic, Harper's, Kenyon Review, Ploughshares, Smokelong Quarterly,* and *Quick Fiction,* among others, and in numerous anthologies such as *Sudden Fiction, Flash Fiction, Flash Fiction Forward, Micro Fiction*, and *You Have To Read This*. She has won three Pushcart Prizes and *Agni Review's* John Cheever Award for Fiction. Painter teaches in the MFA Program at Emerson College in Boston. Her collection of flash fiction, *Wouldn't You Like to Know*, was published by Carnegie Mellon in August, 2010.

Rae Bryant's short story collection, *The Indefinite State of Imaginary Morals,* was released from Patasola Press, NY in June 2011 and has been nominated for the Pen Hemingway award. Her stories have appeared in *BLIP Magazine* (formerly *Mississippi Review*), *Opium Magazine*, and *PANK*, among other publications. She has work forthcoming in *Story Quarterly, Puerto del Sol,* and *Gargoyle Magazine* among other journals. Rae has received Fellowships from the VCCA and Johns Hopkins University, where she earned a Masters in Writing and where she now teaches multimedia and creative writing. Read more at www.raebryant.com.

Roxane Gay lives and writes in the Midwest.

Sara Lippmann is a freelance writer and editor. Her fiction has appeared in *Women Arts Quarterly, Smokelong, Our Stories, The Brooklyner, Slice Magazine* and other publications. She co-hosts the Sunday Salon, a NYC reading series, and lives with her family in Brooklyn.

Sherrie Flick is the author of the flash fiction chapbook *I Call This Flirting* (Flume) and the novel *Reconsidering Happiness* (Bison Books). She lives in Pittsburgh, where she writes and teaches and edits and gardens and cooks. www.sherrieflick.com

Tara Laskowski lives in Northern Virginia. She is a senior editor for *SmokeLong Quarterly* and has been published in a variety of places, most recently *Mid-American*

Review and PANK magazine. Her short story collection manuscript, *Black Diamond City*, won the Santa Fe Writers Project 2010 Literary Awards Series. She can be fond online at www.taralaskowksi.com.

Tara L. Masih is editor of *The Rose Metal Press Field Guide to Writing Flash Fiction* (a ForeWord Book of the Year) and author of *Where the Dog Star Never Glows* (a National Best Books Award finalist). She has published fiction, poetry, and essays in numerous anthologies and literary magazines (including *Confrontation, Hayden's Ferry Review, Natural Bridge, The Pedestal, Night Train,* and *The Caribbean Writer*). Her flash appears in several limited edition illustrated chapbooks published by The Feral Press and has been anthologized in *Word of Mouth: 150 Short-Short Stories by 90 Women Writers* and in *Brevity & Echo*. Awards for her work include first place in *The Ledge Magazine*'s fiction contest, a Pushcart Prize, *Best New American Voices*, and Best of the Web nominations. www.taramasih.com.

Casey Hannan haunts a house in Kansas City with his ghost boyfriend, his ghost snake, and the occasional ghost roommate. He writes ghost stories and crochets bodies to inhabit. His novella, *Ghost Here*, will be published in 2013 by Tiny Hardcore Press. Casey accounts for his time at www.casey-hannan.com.

Christopher Allen's fiction and non-fiction have appeared in numerous places like (and unlike) *The Smoking Poet, The Legendary* and *Wilderness House Literary Review*. He was a finalist at Glimmer Train in April 2011, and he blogs about his obsession with seeing the entire planet at www.imustbeoff.blogspot.com.

Curtis Smith's most recent books are *Bad Monkey* (stories, Press 53), *Truth or Something Like It* (novel, Casperian Books), and *Witness* (essays, Sunnyoutside).

Devan Goldstein's writing has appeared in *The Collagist, Annalemma, Bluestem,* and elsewhere. He has edited for *Flywheel Magazine, Everyday Fiction,* and a special issue of *PANK,* and works as a web usability consultant.

Eric Bosse has published stories in *The Sun, Mississippi Review, Zoetrope ASE, Exquisite Corpse, Wigleaf, The Collagist,* and *Night Train,* among others. He lives in Norman with his wife and children and teaches writing at the University of Oklahoma. His collection of stories, *Magnificent Mistakes,* was published in 2011 by Ravenna Press.

J. Bradley is a contributing writer to *Specter Magazine* and the Interviews Editor of *PANK* Magazine. He lives at iheartfailure.net.

Kenneth Pobo has a chapbook of "tweet fiction" forthcoming from Deadly Chaps (fall, 2011) called *Tiny Torn Maps.* He also has a chapbook of poetry (fall, 2011) from Green Fuse Press called *Contralto Crows.* He teaches creative writing and English at Widener University.

Len Kuntz is a writer from Washington State. His work appears widely in print and online at such places as *Housefire, Prick of the Spindle, Verse Wisconsin* and also at lenkuntz.blogspot.com

Marc Nieson is a graduate of the Iowa Writers' Workshop and NYU FilmSchool. Excerpts from SCHOOLHOUSE: A MEMOIR IN 13 LESSONS have appeared in *LiteraryReview, Iowa Review, Green MountainsReview,* and *Chautauqua.* Recent fiction is in *Conjunctions,* and has won a Raymond Carver Short Story award and a Pushcart Prize nomination. His award-winning feature screenplays include BOTTOMLAND, THE

DREAM CATCHER, and THE SPEED OF LIFE. He serves on the faculty of Chatham University, and is working on a new novel, *Houdini's Heirs*.

Marc Schuster is the author of *The Singular Exploits of Wonder Mom and Party Girl* (The Permanent Press 2011) and *The Grievers* (The Permanent Press 2012).

Michael Martone's new book is *Four for a Quarter, fictions*. Recent work includes Racing in Place, essays; Double-wide, collected early fiction; and Michael Martone, a memoir done in contributor's notes like this one.

Nathan Alling Long has numerous stories and essays published in anthologies and literary journals, including *Tin House, Glimmer Train, Story Quarterly, The Sun,* and *Indiana Review*. His work has appeared on NPR and has won him a Truman Capote Fellowship, a Mellon Foundation Fellowship, and a Pushcart nomination. He lives in Philadelphia and teaches at Richard Stockton College of NJ.

Peter Schwartz's poetry has been featured in *PANK*, *Opium*, and *The Columbia Review*. He's also a flash writer, artist, comedian, and dedicated kayaker.

Randall Brown is the author of the award-winning flash fiction collection *Mad to Live* (Flume Press 2008), a collection that has been recently republished by PS Books in Philadelphia as a Deluxe Edition with "bonus tracks" (PS Books 2011). He directs and teaches at Rosemont College's MFA in Creative Writing program. He's been published widely, both online and in print. He is also the founder of Matter Press and its *Journal of Compressed Creative Art*; and he blogs regularly at FlashFiction.Net.

Robert Swartwood's most recent collection of flash fiction is *Phantom Energy*. Visit him at www.robertswartwood.com.

Robert Vaughan's plays have been produced in N.Y.C., L.A., S.F., and Milwaukee where he resides. He leads two writing roundtables for Redbird- Redoak Studio. His prose and poetry is published in over 150 literary journals such as *Elimae, Metazen and BlazeVOX*. He is a fiction editor at *JMWW* magazine, and Thunderclap! Press. He co-hosts Flash Fiction Fridays for *WUWM*'s Lake Effect. His blog: http://rgv7735.wordpress.com.

Rusty Barnes lives in Revere, MA. He is the author of two story collections, most recently *Mostly Redneck*, and the co-founder of *Night Train*, an online journal of literature. He also curates Fried Chicken and Coffee (www.friedchickenandcoffee.com).

Sean Lovelace is the author of the award-winning flash fiction collection, *How Some People Like Their Eggs*, by Rose Metal Press. His newest book is *Fog Gorgeous Stag*, from Publishing Genius Press. He likes to run, far.

Scott Garson is the author of *American Gymnopédies*. He edits *Wigleaf.*

Sheldon Lee Compton survives in Eastern Kentucky. His work has appeared in several journals and anthologies and has been nominated for storySouth Million Writers Award, Best of the Web and the Pushcart Prize.

William Henderson lives outside of Boston, where he can be found tooling around with his children, Avery and Aurora; blogging (hendersonhouseofcards.wordpress.com); tweeting (@Avesdad); practicing yoga and running; writing (always writing); and waiting for what's on the other side of the bridge. He has been published in more than 50 literary journals and magazines, contributes columns to *Specter Literary Magazine; Hippocampus Magazine; Peripheral*

Surveys+, and *Black Fox Lit. NAP Literary Magazine* will release Henderson's first Chapbook in January 2012, and Henderson will be included in the forthcoming anthology, The Other Man. He can be reached at wil329@yahoo.com.